DOCTOR! DOCTOR!

DOCTOR! DOCTOR!

An Insider's Guide to the Games Doctors Play

by

MICHAEL O'DONNELL

illustrated by
Raymond Hitchcock

To Dave

Happy new year

Michael O'Donnell

LONDON
VICTOR GOLLANCZ LTD
1986

First published in Great Britain 1986
by Victor Gollancz Ltd,
14 Henrietta Street, London WC2E 8QJ

British Library Cataloguing in Publication Data
O'Donnell, Michael, *1928–*
   Doctor! Doctor!: an insider's guide to
   the games doctors play.
   1. Social medicine
   I. Title
   362.1   RA418

ISBN 0-575-03874-8

Photoset in Great Britain by
Rowland Phototypesetting Ltd, Bury St Edmunds, Suffolk
and printed by St Edmundsbury Press Ltd
Bury St Edmunds, Suffolk

For Bernard Dixon, Paul Vaughan, Geoff Watts, Charles Coppard, Colin Tudge, Fred Kavalier, Joleen Huckle, Fiona Pearson, Peter Brock, Tim Albert, Bryan Brooke, Jeremy Lawrence, Anne Kellett, Peter Bunyard, and Barbara Evans, in memory of an adventure. The thin ice eventually gave way but the journey was great fun while it lasted.

ACKNOWLEDGEMENTS

Most of the ideas developed in this book were originally floated in the *British Medical Journal* and I doubt I shall ever redeem the debt I owe its editor, Dr Stephen Lock, who granted me the indulgence of the first regular signed column in that journal's history.

I am also grateful to the publishers for permission to include in "The medical student game: 1949" material that first appeared in *My Medical School* published by Robson Books.

CONTENTS

Dangerous games

THERE'S A DOCTOR CLOSE BEHIND YOU

WHEN THE FIRST Rubik cube popped from its manufacturer's mould you can be sure some doctor was at hand, eye bright and pen primed, eager to publish the first condemnatory account of Cuber's Wrist.

The censorious game is an ancient medical tradition—some doctors are still uncertain whether they approve of sex—but the commonest version played today was shaped during the 1950s, with the coming of the hula hoop. Doctors discovered then that if they issued gloomy warnings about what hooping could do to the spine, not only did they get their letters into their professional journals but their names into the sort of newspapers read by their patients.

They needed little further encouragement and recently, for instance, we've had grave pronouncements about Jogger's Nipple, Break-dancing Neck, Crab-eaters Lung, Swim-goggle Headache, and Amusement Slide Anaphylaxis. Indeed, in the index of the *New England Journal of Medicine*, which has become the official journal of the game, you can find Cyclist's Pudendum, Dog Walker's Elbow, Space Invaders' Wrist, Unicyclist's Sciatica, Jeans Folliculitis, Jogger's Kidney, Flautist's Neuropathy, and Urban Cowboy's Rhabdomyolosis—a painful nastiness in the muscles caused by riding mechanical bucking broncos in amusement arcades.

Censorious gamesters seem particularly to enjoy knocking activities promoted by their heartier colleagues. There's an eagerness, for instance, in the way they record the afflictions of joggers, bombarding medical journals with reports of muscle and joint injuries, heart attacks, asthma, and amenorrhoea. Some sort of prize must surely go to the three punctilious Swiss who, in December 1984, reported yet another jogging hazard: bird attacks by the European Buzzard (*Buteo buteo*). Drs Itin, Heanel and Stalder from Kantonsspital Liestal described how the attacks came during the buzzard breeding season and how "the birds attacked by diving from behind and continuing to dive as long as the joggers were in motion". Sadly they didn't speculate on what was passing through the buzzards' minds at the time.

With doctors revelling so brazenly in the role of gloomy killjoy, small wonder that patients flock to fringe medicine and beyond in search of the homely optimism that once radiated from Tannochbrae. In the land of the cliché, prevention may be better than cure but, back in the real world, the punters warm more readily to dear old Dr Cameron than to finger-wagging Dr Snoddie. Medicine must not blind itself to the wisdom of great men like Mr Robert Robinson, who have said that they hope their doctors will keep any bad news to them-selves. Optimism has always been powerful therapy and I have often seen optimistic doctors help patients fight off—even overcome—the effects of incurable disease.

Optimism also enhances a doctor's reputation. When his patients die, friends and relatives will say: "The doctor was marvellous. He did all that was humanly possible but Nature beat him in the end." His reputation always outshines that of the medical pessimist whose patients never die "despite his efforts". Even worse, they occasionally survive despite his efforts. The world is full of gleeful old fogies eager to de-scribe how they cheated their pessimistic doctors. They wave their walking-sticks and tell us proudly how, maybe 40 years before, some gloomy killjoy gave them only six months to live.

Optimism, I am convinced, is an essential component of that ephemeral quality possessed by doctors whom patients feel better for seeing, no matter what treatment is prescribed. Such doctors are often assumed to be endowed with gifts denied to their colder hearted colleagues but 30 years of casual doctor-watching have persuaded me that the "gift" is largely a tech-nique. Given the right technique, today's gloomy denouncer of cream cakes, coffee, and BMX bicycles could transmogrify overnight into dear old Dr Cameron.

The best techniques are rarely written down but are passed by word of mouth within the brotherhood or handed down as heirlooms from doctor fathers to their doctor sons. The most valuable one I know was passed to me by the grandson of a distinguished Dublin physician, Richard Leeper. It went something like this: "Never give medicine to a dying man. Always give him brandy. Everyone knows that brandy never harmed anyone but give the patient medicine and someone will say: 'God forgive me if I wrong him, but the doctor's draught was the last thing the poor man took.'"

Grandfather Leeper must have received that advice round about 1880 and no one knows how many generations it had passed through before it reached him. It could well have started with Hippocrates, for that quality of learning has an imperishable validity.

THE AMERICAN DREAM GAME

PLASTIC SURGEONS NOW stand poised to replace psychiatrists as purveyors of the American Dream. Every day, it
seems, more Americans realize it is not inhibitions that are
holding them back but baggy eyelids, baldness, or sagging
boobs. Physical image is now as important as mental cleanli-
ness, and success is not so much a matter of letting it all hang
out as of having it all tucked in. I speak dogmatically because
I have become an addicted spectator of a game which, to a
British doctor, is the medical equivalent of American Football:
U.S. cosmetic surgery. My favourite overseas relaxation is to
attend conventions of American cosmetic surgeons where the
high seriousness of the scientific programme is invariably
enhanced by the whispered observations exchanged in the
hotel lobbies.

"Guess whose nose he just got . . . There goes the boob king
of San Diego . . . That guy's reslung half the asses in Beverly
Hills." The very length of the limousines that queue to collect
their owners at the end of the day fuel the American suspicion
that cosmetic surgery gamesters are doctors who train to do
good, then learn to do well.

During the conventions, the stands in the exhibition hall do
a brisk trade in aids to self-advertisement that would never
come under starter's orders with Britain's General Medical
Council. On the back of your "customized visiting card"—what
on earth is a non-customized one?—you can have a cartoon of
an ape-faced man saying: "Don't envy a good complexion, buy
one", or of a woman—blonde, of course—sitting *en negligée*
before her dressing-table saying: "Mirror, mirror on the wall
. . . lie to me."

Occasionally at a convention I've found evidence of cosmetic
overkill. One evening in the bar I happened upon a bunch of
surgeons and their wives and girl friends. At first glance, the
women were stunningly attractive, until I got the message.
When a girl hitches up with a cosmetic surgeon, she becomes
a walking, talking advertisement of his skill. There wasn't a
wrinkle in sight, not even on the petite blonde doll whose
ball-gown seemed to have been fashioned from a fisherman's

net of none too narrow a mesh, presumably to show off her guy's overall competence. The effect was detumescent. I was suddenly reminded of those aloof ladies who, when I was an adolescent, posed in their underwear on London Underground posters and whose breasts and thighs seemed sculpted from ice.

The most relaxed gamesters at the conventions are those who enjoy their speciality's racy image. Most of them practise in Southern California or are lazy-accented Southerners who tend to the cosmetic needs of folk of the ilk of the J. R. Ewings. The Californians have few hang-ups about their work. But then,

neither do their patients. David Niven once described how he
embarked on a throwaway remark at a dinner party: "You can
always tell a woman's plastic surgeon by the cut of her . . ." He
had the attention of all seven faces around the table and
realized with horror that each one bore that uncreased smile
that only a surgeon can hitch into place. Then he remembered
he was in Southern California and relaxed. Few people there
have inhibitions about their cosmetic operations. Dammit all,
the surgery is so expensive you want folks to know you can
afford it.

In Southern California, a woman who has had a face job, a
nose job, a chin job, or a boob job will give a cocktail party for
her plastic surgeon just as soon as the scars have healed, and
invite her friends round so she can show off what he's done for
her. The surgeons, whose role hovers uneasily twixt that of
doctor and gigolo, are delighted to attend because these show-off
parties are where they recruit most of their future customers
. . . a sort of surgical Tupperware technique.

The Californian approach to cosmetic surgery derives naturally from the cult of youth that prevails in the Southern end
of that state. In Santa Monica, for instance, you qualify for a
senior citizen's pass at the age of 50. Few citizens apply. But
the cult doesn't travel well. One of the more depressing features
of New York evenings is the sight of men in Manhattan mid-
town bars, weary after a day in the office, yet striving dangerously to live up—or, more accurately, down—to the age of their
hair transplants. In truth, the chase in Southern California is
not so much after youth as after the energy that youth bestows
and the chase is seductive for visitors from staider territory.
The only cosmetic surgery a visiting Briton needs is an unstiff-
ening of the upper lip.

I enjoy Californians' openness about their emotions especially
when they are attractive, young, and female. (Deep down—
well, not all that deep down—I disapprove of sexism but occasionally my id gets the better of me.) At parties in Surrey,
people who discover I was once a proper doctor tell me: "You'll
be very interested in my back (or knee, or bowels)". In California
they say: "Let me tell you somethin' 'bout this emotional problem (hang-up, crazy relationship) I got". And while they tell
me they often, if they're female, hold my hand between theirs

and stroke it. A spoilsport psychiatrist told me they do this because they have dysphoric histroid characteristics. When I looked that up in a U.S. medical dictionary, I discovered that "the subjects are usually female, man-centred, rejection-sensitive, and contrectation-minded." Contrectation? In American psychiatry, not only are they profligate with their hyphens but one dictionary always leads to another. Contrectation, I discovered, means: "Touching or stroking a member of the opposite sex. Usually refers to the first stage of sexual arousal." California is clearly the home of descriptive rather than explanatory psychiatry but I can understand how constant exposure to this stroking business could encourage a chap with an adolescent libido locked up in a middle-aged frame to consider the merits of a hair transplant.

I got a solider psychiatric opinion from a British expatriate, Bruce Sloame, who is chairman of the Department of Psychiatry at the University of Southern California. He explained why first psychotherapy and now cosmetic surgery are logical adjuncts to the American Dream, by referring to the Saniflush concept of psychotherapy. This depends on everyone believing that they have it within themselves to achieve greatness if only some therapist or guru can flush out those hang-ups and inhibitions that get in the way and hold them back. Until the day of the great national Saniflush, I'm happy to accept things as they are. Every time I'm on a plane to the West Coast, I hear the adolescent who lies buried within my aging frame quietly humming: "Open up those Golden Gates, Contrectation here I come."

THE LEGACY GAME

IN DECEMBER 1956 Dr John Bodkin Adams, a fashionable Eastbourne GP and a respected pillar of his local church, was arrested and charged with the murder of an eighty-year-old lady who had been one of his patients. Four months later—a period during which newspapers had published gossip and innuendo suggesting Bodkin Adams enticed old ladies to write him into their wills and then murdered them—an old Bailey jury took only 40 minutes to find him not guilty. When Adams died in 1983, one beneficiary named in his will was the former chief crime reporter of the *Daily Express*, Percy Hoskins, who, during the inventive speculation that flourished before and during the trial, was the only Fleet Street crime reporter at all sympathetic to the doctor's own version of events. Lord Beaverbrook, proprietor of the *Express*, had allowed Hoskins to pursue his independent line but grew increasingly worried that his paper had got it wrong. When the jury announced its verdict, Beaverbrook sent Hoskins a telegram addressed, the story goes, to El Vino's, the Fleet Street wine bar. The telegram read: "Two men have been acquitted today."

The style of general practice that emerged as the Bodkin Adams story unfolded led people to conclude he had only one motive: the one of which he was acquitted at the Old Bailey. Like Percy Hoskins, I was less sure because, while doing a GP locum in the nineteen-fifties, I had encountered the Legacy Game—a style of practice that made the publicized events in Eastbourne at least understandable, if not acceptable. I had to look after the patients of a GP who seemed to specialize in the care of wealthy widows and who had earned his nickname: "the legacy doctor". One of his great selling points was that he had refused to join the NHS because its nasty socialist rules prevented him giving his patients truly personal care—though he had enough respect for NHS benefits to recommend his flock to register with local GPs so that they could get their drugs free on NHS prescription.

My experience of his practice came when he fell ill and I happened to be doing a locum for one of the NHS GPs he'd involved in his "arrangement" for prescriptions. This meant the NHS doctors were legally responsible for his patients' care and, for one month, I was assigned the "legacy doctor's" Regular Visits—a group of patients whom he visited at the same time each week, each fortnight, or each month. All of them had been on the Regular List for at least a year, many for ten years, and one had had a weekly bedside consultation for the previous 22 years. Most were women whose tycoon husbands had despatched themselves to an early grave accumulating the wealth that their widows now frittered away on frivolities: expensive hairdressers, expensive boxes of chocolates, expensive flower arrangements, and expensive regular visits from an expensive private doctor. My biggest problem was trying to discover the topics on which I was expected to converse during the hour allotted to each on my timetable. I soon discovered the one thing they didn't want was any form of clinical examination . . . other than my holding their wrist in pulse-taking mode while they told me long rambling self-centred stories.

The condition their GP was treating was, of course, loneliness —though I was never quite sure whether he was treating it or exploiting it. I hadn't the courage to do aught but maintain the status quo till he returned but I had plenty of time to analyse his technique. The profitable Regular Visit was based on the early establishment of an Agreed Illness. The ideal Agreed Illness was one not too incapacitating to interfere with the pleasures of a well-upholstered life, yet serious enough to need regular attention and to allow for an occasional spectacular "attack" that demanded dramatic medical intervention and sympathetic clucking from sycophantic friends.

The most popular Agreed Illnesses were afflictions of the liver and alimentary tract—particularly the colon—and in setting them up, the "legacy doctor" had avoided too precise an aetiology. Most involved something that had "slipped"—womb, stomach, intervertebral disc, even an occasional rib—but there were a lot of "floating kidneys" and impressive yardages of surplus bowel. Three patients (I secretly hoped they would meet one day) told me: "Dr Handholder says I have the longest colon he's ever seen on an X-ray". Another popular Agreed Illness was low blood pressure, which had the advantage of being the antithesis of something suffered by the common herd. Those who wished their ailments to be touched by science had settled for "sluggish metabolism" or "disturbed biochemistry". The ideal Agreed Illness had to be specific both to patient and doctor. The patient, when talking to impressionable friends, had to be able to say: "My liver (kidney/womb/metabolism) is unique, you know. Every doctor, and I've seen the very best, my dear, has been quite baffled by my X-rays." But unless she could add, "Indeed, they're so complicated that only dear Dr Handholder can understand them", dual specificity had not been established and the patient could, after a minor tiff, take her profitable illness elsewhere. Even I could see that lack of dual specificity inhibited market expansion, since the impressionable friends of today would be the Regular Visits of tomorrow.

Though clinical examination was tabu on regular visits, a private prescription was mandatory. (NHS ones for real drugs for unagreed illnesses were, as I've explained, supplied irregularly by other doctors.) The Agreed Prescription was always a mixture of at least six innocuous items; any fewer would have been unimposing when written on the prescription and any active ingredient might have produced an unpleasant physiological effect. The mixture also had to have an unpleasant taste. Regular Visits had a masochistic streak. They were born to suffer from the Agreed Illness and relief came only out of tribulation.

The other standard treatment was the Agreed Injection, usually of Cytamen and its pink colour helped it to home in, vigorously, on the placebo receptors. I suspected an Agreed Injection had converted many a patient from an occasional to a Regular Visit because injections never came singly but in courses, no course had a predetermined length, and no course could be effective without an unspecified number of reinforcing courses.

I'm not suggesting that Dr Bodkin Adams practised in that way, but my month's tuition in the legacy game introduced me to the sort of patients he must have had to treat. I regard my experience as of purely historical interest. No one these days could get away with such unprincipled chicanery. Or could they?

Party games

THE ANALYSIS GAME

"It was the carrots that did it," said the woman behind me on the Southbound platform at Goodge Street station. "He never did anything kinky till he started eating those carrots. I reckon they put him in mind of it." An inconsiderate train rattled in and drowned my eavesdropping. But I recognized the game that was being played. It was a low level version of the Analysis Game in which players elaborate theories about human behaviour. In First Division clashes, the points go to those who use the least experimental evidence yet provoke the most cries of "What a clever idea!" from the spectators.

There's nothing new about this particular trivial pursuit. I'm sure the more imaginative cave-man played it to relax after a hard day drawing bison on the wall. But it was left to Freud to devise the game's Culbertson conventions and endow it with the social cachet it once shared with *Times* crossword puzzling and "serious" bridge. In its heyday the game removed the drama from Oedipus and the fun from sex, and ensured that those versatile acrobats Ego and Id were good for an evening's bouncing on the conversational trampoline.

The game took a firmer grip on American doctors than on British ones—'twas said in the nineteen fifties that "analysis" was the only way American patients could get to talk to a doctor—but the Goodge Street conversation sent me back to a work that has lain too long upon my bookshelves, the seminal paper that gave the first hint that the game had lost its bourgeois status and had become a kick-about which anyone could join. It is an article headed "Understanding sexual attraction"

written by Our Psychologist in one of those magazines they
thrust into your hands if you arrive at a London terminus on
a commuter train. Our Psychologist's first move in the game is
this: "Female breasts appeal to men because their shape mimics
the buttocks, which are obvious zones of erotic interest." And
a sharp no-nonsense opener it is too. No concessions there
to perverts who might find breasts attractive because they
resemble breasts or bottoms attractive because they resemble
bottoms. Yet the allure of the Analysis Game is such that, no
matter how outraged you are by your opponents' propositions,
you feel compelled to riposte. The first time I read the breast/
buttock hypothesis, I found myself responding: "The female
umbilicus attracts the male because it resembles the foxhole
in which every man would like to hide to protect himself

from an anxiety-ridden world." And, once you tune in to the wavelength, profundities can spill from your lips like imitation pearls popping out of their polythene moulds. How about: "A man may be attracted by a nurse's uniform because it reminds him of the midwife who, at his birth, severed the only attachment he had to his mother."

The best moves, though, are those that extend your opponent's observations. When Our Psychologist writes "Female legs are triggers to sexual response because they lead to potential delights", an experienced player will reply: "Depends on which way you're travelling. Or is a foot fetishist a chap who took the wrong turning at his mother's knee?"

And though the game has moved down market, the bourgeoisie has not abandoned it. Indeed it still provides the most serious minded players. We still have magistrates who *know* why others sin and who read them pious homilies while they stand in the dock. Just as we still have MPs who *know* it is pornography that drives men to lustful acts and not lust that drives men to pornography. That sort of certainty develops all too easily when the traditional game is played too often in the wrong company, so I have invented a variation designed especially for doctors, particularly those whose scepticism needs rehabilitation.

To launch the game, I concoct a bizarre proposition and then invite them to explain their patients' behaviour in terms of it. I might start, for instance, by proposing that the driving force in Man is an unquenchable desire to eat stewed prunes and custard. What follows? How about "The black and gold furnishings of ancient Egypt were a blatant expression of the colours of the Life Force"? Or "A predilection for a blonde or brunette sexual partner is an individual's attempt to compensate for an inbuilt imbalance at the prune/custard nexus", "White racists are driven by a puritanical fervour to deny the attraction of a black skin", "Oedipus married his mother because of her wrinkles". They are but the first thoughts that seem to flow. (Gosh, could that use of the verb flow be a Custardian slip?) A couple of rounds a year could ensure both doctors and their patients stay enwrapped in a healthy cloak of scepticism. We need that protection every bit as much as did the cavemen.

NATIONAL HEALTH PARTY GAMES

WHEN SOME WELL intentioned citizen organized a huge children's party in Hyde Park, a friend of mine volunteered to assist.

"What was it like?" I asked.

"A bit like Alfred Hitchcock's *The Birds*," she said, "but with children instead of birds."

I sympathized. I'm now an old hand at the party game but they never quite lose their terror. When my elder daughter reached the age of eighteen, her planning of her birthday party concerned only the security arrangements. She expected raids from gatecrashers and police and her most earnest hope was that both would arrive at the same time.

When she was six, only her mother and I felt threatened. And then the threat was not to our personal safety—or so we thought—but to our rating in the local parent charts. On that historic sixth birthday, I tried to allay my anxiety by drawing up a chart of objectives, organization, and methods. I even bought a book of instructions. With the help of the birthday girl and her four-year-old sister I made my preparations. "Pre-planning", said my book, "is the secret of a successful party." (I had no time to consider what post-planning might be.)

When D-day dawned fine and clear, it dawned on a garden transformed into what the book called a "well-planned party area". We had marked out tracks for three-legged, sack, and potato races, had filled the paddling pool with clean water, and concealed expensive Treasure Trail trophies in the shrubbery.

Meanwhile, my wife had manned the kitchen with a quiet efficiency, buttering rolls, cutting sandwiches, frying sausages, de-moulding psychedelic blancmanges, and stacking the refrigerator with bricks of ice-cream and a kaleidoscopic collection of fruit drinks. By D-day lunchtime O'Donnell's suburban castle was equipped and provisioned to withstand the most rigorous assault.

The enemy started to infiltrate our position round about 15.30 hours. They looked innocent enough in their billowing party frocks, silk ribbons, lace stockings, and best shoes. Tired-eyed parents, veterans of tough campaigns fought over their own territory, dumped their charges on our doorstep and scurried away smiling mysterious smiles. Poor fools, I thought. D-day holds no fears for the man who pre-plans.

By 15.45 we had the enemy at our mercy, cornered in the sitting room. All presents had been opened and cooed over, and the wrapping paper neatly stowed away. Admittedly, four toys were already broken but a wise general knows he will suffer early casualties in even his best planned campaign. We were ready to move into Phase One. I flung open the french windows to reveal the pre-planned paradise that lay outside. There was a sizzling flash of lightning, a cataclysmic clap of thunder, and rain descended with a ferocity whose like I'd seen only once before and that in the middle of the Burmese jungle.

Half the children, frightened by the lightning, burst into tears, and demanded to be taken home; the other half dashed through the doors, danced merrily in the rain and then, mustering like the Gadarene swine, plunged into the paddling pool. Within fifteen seconds Phase One had crumbled to tearful and bedraggled disaster. For a moment I almost lost control. Then I marshalled my reserve forces from the kitchen, all the towels from the airing cupboard, and a bizarre collection of discarded childwear that had been put on one side for the Brownies' Jumble Sale. By 16.10 hours we had dried and reclothed the Gadarene and were ready to move direct to Phase Two, indoor games.

But we reckoned without the second echelon. While we were busy mopping up, the non-Gadarene had wiped away their tears and found that time hung heavily upon their hands. First they broke the pick-up arm from the record player, eliminating at a stroke musical bumps, musical chairs, musical anything. Next they cut the hired Mickey Mouse film into fifteen separate skipping ropes, and then with cool efficiency defused our ultimate weapon by squeezing three packets of plasticine through the rear grid of the television set.

I had committed the unforgivable military crime. I had underestimated the enemy.

Yet, as I teetered on the brink of defeat, all those prayers my mother used to say for me homed in on their objective: only divine guidance could have led me to the game I then initiated and which has since become *de rigueur* at medical children's parties, the National Health game.

First we split the enemy into three groups of "NHS doctors". GPs were given ballpoint pens and a limitless supply of paper, and competed to see who could write most before the bell rang for the next patient; consultants played charades among themselves; medical officers of health (as they were then) were sent upstairs for a short lie down. Every half-hour each group changed roles and we controlled the complicated routine by threatening transgressors with the dreaded varicose veins waiting list, which meant they had to stand in the hall for a long, long time.

From there on the games invented themselves: Pin the tail on Kenneth Robinson; Hunt the geriatric bed; Pass the buck; Cross the picket line. Our big finish was the Grand Treatment bonanza, an up-market version of Doctors and Nurses to which I contributed all the bandages, cotton wool, lint, gauze, and splints I could find in the surgery.

At 18.00 hours parents collected their children and at 18.15 I sprawled in an armchair clutching a long, strong drink.

"That," said my wife, "was everything a children's party should be. Original, exciting, and educational."

As she spoke, the phone rang. Sally had had a lovely time, said her mother, especially in the treatment game. She thought she should just check that it was all right for a child of six to swallow twenty of those green tablets.

I reached wearily for the car keys. Absolute victory, it seems, is rarely won without cost.

They turned out to have been Smarties.

LET ME TELL YOU WHO YOU ARE

THE THING I best remember was the sky, a shroud of seamless grey that made you wonder whether there really was a sun beyond it. Drawn low over South London's urban landscape, as it was that Monday morning, it would have depressed the most eupeptic of men. In an office near the top of a highish-rise block, my new boss had just told me to clear my desk by the end of the day and remove myself from a job I'd done for over fifteen years. I'd had no warning. I thought I'd been invited for a friendly discussion of editorial plans.

"Is that it?" I asked. At least, I think I asked. I don't have perfect recall.

The grey man who had pronounced my sentence didn't answer. He just nodded to his familiar who opened the door for me to leave. As I walked through the door, I turned to the familiar who throughout had played a silent role like a chaperone in a GP's surgery and, in a desperate attempt at chirpiness, asked: "How many people walk out of this office and jump straight out of that window?"

He gave a po-faced answer: "They can't. That window's sealed."

Enough time has passed, I think, for me to review that morning in a more detached mood than the depression into which it precipitated me, and to see that the probable reason for the harshness and insensitivity was that, in the eyes of the grey businessman, I was a threat. He assumed that I would go off and play the game that any sensible businessman would play and try ruthlessly to do him down. He wasn't to know, because he'd never really met me, that I wasn't a businessman but a woolly-minded writer—a writer, what's more, whose soft centre had hypertrophied during twelve years in clinical practice. I was about as much a threat to him as a staphylococcus is to a bottle of lysol.

It was a neat comuppance for a doctor, because I suspect many of us play an unconscious game in which we impose on patients our own ideas of what their jobs, their lives, their motivation may be. I'll confess that when I was a GP and patients told me they were, say, business executives or television directors, I rather fancied I knew what their job was like and the stresses and strains to which it subjected them. Until

I learned better, I even presumed to instruct them on what they should or should not do, basing my instruction, I now know, on what I *thought* their lives were like.

Since I've moved out of clinical medicine and seen other worlds at closer quarters, I've learned how false were my outsider's impressions—not grossly false but wrong enough about detail for me not to understand what the work really involved —and I shudder at the presumption I showed when I dished out dogmatic advice on the basis of such ignorance. I was in the position of an orthopaedic surgeon I once watched giving a butcher with a smashed shoulder a detailed and impressive demonstration of how, in future, he should swing his cleaver. The patient was too embarrassed to explain that he worked in the accounts department. Small wonder that patients complain not just that their doctors don't explain but that they don't "understand".

Some years ago I happened upon a physical version of the same misunderstanding. One evening during the second act of *Schwanda the Bagpiper*—a detail of quite stunning irrelevance —I got a nasty pain in my belly. At that stage of my life I must have seen and diagnosed well over 100 cases of acute appendicitis and, in doing so, had created in my mind a picture of what the pain must feel like and the way it moved. When I got the pain myself it was so unlike my picture of it that, at first, I didn't recognize it. Only when I described it to someone did I find I was using the words that patients had used to me. In the past, I had not, as I thought, been recognizing the entity but the patient's description of it.

I wish the revelation had come earlier in my career. Too late I understood that, as doctors, we are at our best when we recognize patterns in other people's behaviour and in what they say to us. We are at our worst when we try to impose patterns of our own making. Within that imposition, I suspect, lie the seeds of medicine's much criticized paternalism or, as they prefer in California, parentalism. I should have remembered advice my GP father gave me soon after I had qualified. I thought he was, as usual, just trying to shock me by contradicting a central lesson drummed into me as a clinical student. "When you've got the hang of general practice," he said, "you'll find the safest thing to do is to make your diagnosis the moment your patient walks into your surgery or you walk into the bedroom. The only reason you take a careful history and perform a painstaking examination is to try to prove yourself wrong."

Later I received the hospital version of the same advice. Confronted with a thick bundle of notes, I was told, go back to the original referring letter from the GP or to the notes made by the admitting houseman who first saw the patient. Those first impressions may contain the answer you are looking for. When recently I told a university lecturer of my father's quirky advice, I learned that the process has been sanctified with an academic name—"pattern recognition". I hope the label doesn't put doctors off learning what it means.

Educational games

THE MEDICAL STUDENT GAME: 1949 VERSION

I PLANNED MY first move in the game in the bar of The Two
Sawyers, the pub that used to stand across the road from the
entrance to St Thomas's Hospital. (I never did discover whether
the commemorated sawyers were woodmen or surgeons.) Only
after I'd carefully fashioned my opening question did I cross
Lambeth Palace Road to the Dean's Office.

"Could this hospital," I asked, "entertain the idea of a part-
time medical student?"

"Is there any other kind?" asked Allen Crockford, secretary
to the Dean.

I'd reached his presence via a Part One in the Cambridge
Natural Sciences Tripos, a Part Two in the Footlights, and a
spell in repertory that convinced me that I'd never make it as
an actor. My Tripos exempted me from second MB and I made
my inquiry of Allen Crockford because, during the weeks I'd
carried a spear into corners of Ireland never before penetrated
by foreign mercenaries, I'd developed a romantic urge to become
an eccentric country GP like Roger Livesey in *A Matter of Life
and Death*.

In those days "grant" was not a word in common usage but
I was earning a few bob writing scripts for comedians like
Robert "Bumper Fun Book" Morton and for BBC radio—television was still a minority sport—and Allen Crockford saw no
reason why I should give up those jobs while I "walked the
wards". (He didn't use the phrase but, even in 1949, others still
did.) In return for his indulgence he extracted an unwritten
promise that I would write the St Thomas's Christmas Show

which before the war had earned the same sort of reputation as the Footlights Revues.

Allen Crockford was keen to expand the medical School's activities and determined to prevent it from becoming just a place for technical instruction. He had a big say in the selection of students and, though he never tried to emulate the St Mary's policy of buying in rugby players with scholarships, he was always on the look-out for scrum halves, musicians for the hospital orchestra, oarsmen, choristers, editors for the St Thomas's gazette, indeed anyone with talent who might occasionally divert other students' attention from their textbooks. He ensured we at least got a chance to develop qualities which today's academic departments are often better at codifying than inculcating. He didn't want St Thomas's students to become a homogeneous group and we ended up heterogeneous almost to a fault. By the time students in my year had qualified, some had played in a team that had won the inter-hospitals rugby, cricket, hockey, or bridge cup, had rowed in a Head of the River crew, or played in an orchestra conducted by the unknown Colin Davis or performed songs written for the Christmas Show by the equally unknown Richard Rodney Bennett.

When I left the Dean's office on the day of my acceptance I walked through the long Central Corridor which ran parallel with the Thames and linked the ward blocks. It was the High Street of the strange community I'd joined, a bustling place where groups and individuals scurried and strolled, paused and intermingled, regrouped and moved on, gossiping or wrapped in thought: patients smart and patients shabby, nurses with status proclaimed in the colour of their belts or the colour of their uniforms, athletic-looking physiotherapists in white coats with brown belts, midwives in blue serge, lab. technicians carrying wire baskets of rubber-bunged test tubes, uniformed porters carrying patients on trolleys, visitors carrying flowers, patients walking, patients limping, patients swathed in bandages, patients motionless on trolleys wrapped in red blankets and attached by rubber tubes to transfusion bottles, doctors in long white coats, doctors in short white coats, doctors hurrying, doctors standing in groups dangling their stethoscopes behind their backs and deep in earnest conversation, hospital maintenance men and painters carrying buckets and brushes and lad-

ders, kitchen porters pushing closed metal trolleys that gave
off a sound of rattling plates and a smell of stew, probationers
pushing trolleys laden with steel bowls and drums of sterilized
dressings and wooden-cased sphygmomanometers, teaching
rounds of consultants and registrars and students on their way
to the wards from their assembly point in the Central Hall
where the marble busts of their forbears, disguised as laurel-
wreathed Greek or Roman nobles, had been swapped around
after so many student parties that nobody knew which was
which, helmeted policemen looking for the canteen, patients in
search of doctors, lady almoners in search of patients, students
in search of the nearest exit . . .

The batch of students I joined in my first clinical year ranged
in age from early twenties to early thirties because most were
ex-servicemen. More than two thirds of us had done our pre-
clinical work at Oxbridge; the others had been through the St
Thomas's pre-clinical school. There were four women in our
year and less than twenty in the medical school. St Thomas's
had been one of the last London teaching hospitals to admit
women and had capitulated only three years before, after resist-
ing change with traditional arguments like not having suitable
lavatories. Some of the ex-service students had led genuinely
adventurous lives and had won battle decorations. Others liked
to titillate those whose experience had been confined to prep
and public school. Eric Wilkes, who later became professor of
general practice at Sheffield, used to claim he'd been a Brigadier
in command of a Mobile Bath Unit.

We also had a few students who were labelled "late vo-
cations". They included a pharmacist who'd leaped over the
counter in middle age and "Pop" Manley, a retired Indian judge
who was in his sixties and preparing himself to be a medical
missionary. He was so deaf that rumour claimed he didn't pass
his finals until he got a case that didn't require him to hear
anything through a stethoscope. On his first appearance in the
operating theatre, his cap and mask obscured his grey hair and
his facial wrinkles. A pompous young surgeon lectured the new
students on surgical etiquette and hinted how lucky they were
to be apprenticed to genius. When he finished, one of them
stepped forward and said: "Now, young man, perhaps you could
explain exactly what you're going to try and do."

We started our clinical careers in Casualty, a word I always found disturbing because I was used to applying it to a person not a place. Casualty was a large white-tiled hall where the afflicted sat and waited on benches or in wheelchairs built like wooden rocking-chairs with the rockers replaced with outsize bicycle wheels. The waiting hall was flanked by smaller rooms, some with names like Medical Sorting Room, others just filled with steaming sterilizers and sinks and draining boards and shelves that bore enormous bottles of pink carbolic fluid. In those side rooms, clad in white gowns tied up at the back, we learned to apply bandages, to lay out trolleys with rubber sheets and instruments, and containers with strange-sounding names like gallipots and porringers, to syringe ears, swab throats, and give injections of penicillin, the new exciting drug which worked magic on the carbuncles, boils and septic fingers our Lambethian patients brought to us in our white-tiled rooms.

Once we could get bandages to stay on fingers (or with greater difficulty on lower legs) long enough for the patient to clear the hospital premises, we were promoted to stitching cuts or even incising abscesses in patients who'd been temporarily asphyxiated with a mixture of gas and air supplied by one of our colleagues. For the sake of scientific appearance the gas supply came from a modern looking machine but the anaesthetic was rarely smooth. Most patients had to be physically restrained and occasionally instruments and gallipots and even a student or two flew across the room. Yet when the patients woke they never remembered anything. If we didn't always achieve anaesthesia we never, thank God, failed to induce amnesia.

Casualty was where we first encountered nightingales—the colloquialism for St Thomas's nurses. The Nightingale School, founded by Florence herself, was reputedly the home of an exclusive religious order for the daughters of top-drawer famil-ies. Even in 1949, we were told, nightingales received direction not to fraternize with medical students. But someone, maybe Hitler, had blown a hole in that tradition and the long hours of the casualty dresser were spiced with mild flirtation; nothing as vulgar as bottom pinching, of course, but lots of significant eye work above the surgical masks and an occasional giggle over the gallipots or the paraffin gauze. Casualty was where we learned one lesson medical students never forget: eyes that enchant above a mask can disenchant at the unmasking. We forged few liaisons in those first months. Those came later when we visited the wards at night and exchanged sweet nothings over Horlicks in the ward kitchen or occasional sweet somethings in the linen cupboard.

In between our spells in Casualty we attended teaching outpatients. Final year students sat in the front rows, were asked questions and examined patients. We sat in the back row and gawped. The patients we saw were not the serendipitous ebb and flow of hospital outpatients but specimens who'd been specially selected because they had unusual lumps or "interesting" conditions. Patients who were "good teaching material" were often given jobs on the staff, as porters or seamstresses so that they would be readily available. I remember being a mite disturbed when the hospital barber, who liked to make flamboyant play with a cut-throat razor, turned up as a specimen at one teaching session and we discovered he suffered from a condition that made him liable to sudden "blackouts". I also remember being angered by the arrogance of some of the registrars who bossed the patients about and showed them off as if they were performing animals. And being equally angered by the way patients, if they were old or poor, were patronizingly referred to as Dad or Mum or Pop or Granny without anyone ever asking them if they liked it. But my anger remained unspoken because ours was a docile generation, used to being told what was good for it through seven years of war.

We also attended lectures in which people like Sharpey-Shafer, the professor of medicine, and his reader Tony Dornhorst tried to convince us that clinical medicine was a science and not a collection of old docs' tales. Tony Dornhorst tried to help us understand the circulation with what he called "an electrical analogy". His equations, laden with symbols, were more baffling than the hydrodynamics they were supposed to simplify, but we could forgive him anything because of the throwaway lines he forced through his stammer. One sleepy summer afternoon he asked a student to name the causes of an enlarged spleen. The student shook himself from half slumber and, playing for time, muttered: "The causes are legion, sir." "Then just give us a co-co-cohort or two," said Tony Dornhorst.

After Casualty we were attached to medical firms and allotted patients on the wards. It needed a rugged determination, and a cultivated insensitivity, to question and examine patients who had already endured both processes at the hands of at least six real doctors. The large, airy wards designed by Florence were surprisingly cosy despite their size; they even had a central fireplace where coal glowed in winter and before which most of the great men warmed their behinds while giving us the benefit. We learned to identify some of the noises we were told we should hear through our stethoscopes and became industrious collectors of sputum, urine and gastric washings. The march of medical science ensured we were also tireless drawers of blood. We chased the vein not with neat and relatively painless syringe needles but with whacking great WR needles. The Ward Sisters insisted that the WR needles prevented us from doing unnecessary damage but I always thought them cruel.

Our firm had two consultants, a posse of registrars, a couple of housemen and eight to ten students. Once we had written up our notes on our patients, often copying and rephrasing what the houseman had already written, we had to mug up answers to the questions we guessed might occur to our consultant when we gave account of our stewardship. That happened on the weekly teaching round. The consultant stopped at any bed that had his name above it in large letters and asked "Whose patient?" The student responsible then stepped forward and tried to establish the required identity: keen yet humble, bright yet deferential. A few succeeded.

Most of the rounds were amiable affairs. The consultant worked through a repertoire of things he thought we ought to learn, of trick questions, and of carefully-burnished jokes which experience had taught him would last the three months we were under his tutelage. Hector Goadby taught us how to examine patients and how to be kind to them. John Harman and John Anderson tried hard to sharpen our wits, and the endearingly eccentric Evans Jones gave frequent noisy examples of just how exciting the diagnosis game could be.

Only one physician played the martinet. There was always tension when Jack Elkington took us round his neurological beds. The student who hadn't done his homework, and occasionally the student who had, was coldly and ruthlessly humiliated before his colleagues. And God help the patient or nurse who made a noise while the great man was talking. One day when we entered the ward, the Elk (inevitable nickname) paused and looked around. Sister had done her work well. Every patient was in bed, neatly lined up with nose the regulation number of inches above the sheet. No bed cover was wrinkled. The nurses stood silently at their posts. No sight nor sound intruded on serenity. The Elk gazed tetchily towards the window.

"The birds are a little noisy this morning Sister," he said.

When we played the traditional student game of deciding whom we would want to treat us if we were ill, most settled for a promising young physician who seemed to know his stuff and was nice with it. His name was John Richardson and he was rumoured to have done something clever in the war though we never found out what it was. Twenty-five years later he became president of the GMC and a member of the House of Lords.

When we finished on the medical wards and did surgery, obstetrics, and "others", we extended our acquaintance with the hospital "characters"—consultants who told good stories or of whom good stories could be told. We also encountered a few less predictable individuals. William Sargant argued with psychotherapeutic passion that psychiatry was merely a matter of applied physiology. Ronnie Furlong taught us orthopaedics in a style that reminded me of Mr Jingle: "Little Willie . . . climbs tree . . . branch breaks . . . put out hand . . . green stick. Grandma falls out of chair . . . dinner fork deformity . . . Colles."

"Pasty" Barrett, witty and perceptive and with a fine line in professional iconoclasm, was an inveterate practical joker. When a fellow chest surgeon, Sir Clement Price Thomas, received the accolade, "Pasty" organized a dinner for him and took me along as a putative representative of the Ministry of Health. When the time came for me to propose the Ministerial tribute I announced that there had been a mix up because I came from the Ministry of Agriculture and Fisheries. I then launched into an old Footlights cabaret performance of a ministerial public-relations man exhorting Britain's trawlermen to improve national kipper productivity. This induced a whole minute of horrified silence before the audience spotted I was sitting next to "Pasty" and guessed they were the subject of a prank. They then became the most appreciative bunch I've ever known.

Richard Gordon had yet to publish *Doctor in the House* but, when he did, we recognized our world. And he reminded us how great a part hierarchy and anecdote played in our lives and in our assessment of people's worth. We were proud of our "characters" and retold their tales with pride. Yet our pride was hopelessly blinkered. We never measured our heroes against those alleged to exist elsewhere. I remember "Pasty" Barrett trying to encourage us to attend lectures at other hospitals but few did.

We also had blind spots about parts of our own hospital which were not on the regular student beat. *Time* magazine took most of us by surprise when it revealed St Thomas's had a figure of international repute. Harold Ridley, the ophthalmic surgeon, had been the first man to replace cataract-damaged lenses with acrylic ones. But few of us had noticed because we'd been too busy listening to the "characters'" stories. Looking back I'm sure we also underestimated the worth of Sharpey-Shafer and people like Geoffrey Bateman whom few recognized as the best surgeon in the hospital because he did ENT in the basement, and Derek Wylie and Harry Churchill Davidson who were busy preparing the textbook that helped establish anaesthesia as a respectable scientific craft.

When my children started to ask me what we looked like in the "olden days", I used to tell them to watch the next television repeat of an Ealing comedy: our hair short and our clothes still wartime utility. Most of us wore grey flannels and tweed jackets, often with leather patches on the elbows. Idiosyncrasy in dress strayed no further than an occasional bow tie or a pair of corduroy trousers. I suspect our accents were pretty uniform, too, the cut-glass sort we heard each day on the BBC. Working-class accents were acceptable in patients but not yet on radio or cinema screen where comic underlings were played by cosy souls like Stanley Holloway or Joyce Grenfell using fractured cut-glass voices.

Conformity was a necessary virtue. Eccentricity was tolerated only if it emerged in a gentlemanly form. Active dissent led to a drying up of sources of privilege and patronage. I wonder how much of the conformity was part of a St Thomas's

tradition and how much was brought back by ex-service
students from their officers' messes. Its observance certainly
involved service-like detail. Two students who didn't wear a
black tie for the full period between King George VI's death
and his interment were subjected to unostentatious yet pointed
ostracism.

A few clinical students lived at home but most of us lived in
digs. St Thomas's House, the students' club across the road
from the hospital, had rooms for students on the upper floors,
but the hospital had taken them over to house foreign workers
employed as ward maids and known, because of the colour of
their uniforms, as Pinkies. Most student digs were in Chelsea,
Battersea, South Kensington or Pimlico. A few intellectuals
commuted from Hampstead, exhaling garlic and reading the
New Statesman, and some lonely souls got stuck in barren
single rooms around Earls Court, though most escaped to share
flats in less chilly parts of town. Shared flats ranged from
well organized households of monastic propriety to notorious
establishments in Battersea and Chelsea where the transient
population often outnumbered the residents and where the
lifestyle was one of dedicated debauchery.

Two set of digs were highly popular because they were just
across the road from the hospital, and students living in them
could have breakfast and dinner in the nurses' dining-room,
though they had to sit at separate tables from the nurses.
Number 79 Lambeth Palace Road was the premier digs with
clean, well-kept rooms. Number 57, where I managed to insinu-
ate myself after three months, was equally convenient to the
hospital but the housekeeping was a furlong or two behind that
of 79.

Each room in 57 was lit by gas delivered to the mantles
through elaborate brass fittings. Heat came from a gas fire.
The supply for both came through a meter which I had to
service with shillings, when times were flush, and pennies,
when times were harder. The establishment was owned and
run by Miss Lang who was old, fat, ponderous and arthritic
but essentially well meaning. Every morning she struggled
wheezing up the stairs with jugs of hot water, and later, when
we were out, with even larger quantities of cold to replenish
the ewers that stood in bowls on our marble washstands. She

also flicked round the rooms with a feather duster, but as she could neither bend nor stretch she managed to clean only a band of wall that started eighteen inches above the skirting board and ended at shoulder height. Above and below those levels the dust settled undisturbed.

I started in the top floor back and spent six weeks learning to sleep through the sound of the night trains running in and out of Waterloo. After seven months I moved to the second floor front and spent another six weeks acclimatizing to the noise of the all night trams as they clattered across the points that lay between 57 and the entrance to Casualty across the road. After I'd been there eighteen months, London Transport stopped the trams and I spent another six weeks learning to sleep through the silence.

Like most of the student rooms in Lambeth Palace Road, number 57's second floor front was alleged to have housed Somerset Maugham when he was a St Thomas's student. It was crammed with Victoriana: a brass fender, a woven table-runner that slid off every time I placed anything near it, a dirty lace antimacassar on the back of a springless uneasy chair and a magnificent brass-knobbed bedstead. In winter I used to freeze in that bed because Miss Lang was frugal with her blankets. I piled overcoats on top of me but because I lay on the thinnest mattress I've ever known, and though Miss Lang had packed layers of newspapers between it and the springs, the cold Lambethian fog seeped upwards and caught me *a tergo*. Still it can't have been too bad because I stayed there till I qualified.

A hundred yards along from 57 was St Thomas's House, always called the Club. Housemen, registrars and an occasional consultant might call in at the bar, which had Scotch Ale on draught, but it was really student territory with its club notice-boards, its ground-floor cafeteria where most of us had lunch, its first-floor lounge where we could loiter reading news-papers and magazines and where obsessional bridge players often started to deal at lunch-time and laid down their last hand at one o'clock the following morning, and its ever helpful, ever resourceful head porter, Sid Mullins.

Sid, more than any member of the medical or nursing staff, was the enduring character in most students' lives. He was a quiet ex-serviceman, lean, dark haired, unostentatious, hard-working and invincibly honest. He showed a remarkable tolerance of the antics indulged in by students at odds with maturity and had a deeply felt loyalty to the medical school. He would inconvenience himself to unbelievable extents to help any student who he thought was trying to help the school; he had little time for those who took the school for granted. He was a daily reminder of how simply some people can interpret the complex notion of integrity.

Five or six times a year the Club lounge was transformed into a ballroom when the cricket, rugby or some other sports club held its annual ball. The card tables, chairs, and most of the sofas were carried upstairs and parked in corridors or downstairs and parked in the dining-room. Spectacular quantities of energy went into decorating the pillared lounge with bunting and balloons, each club trying to outdo all others in the extravagance of its ideas and the effort expended to achieve them.

Come the night of the ball, dinner-jacketed and long-dressed participants rolled in after dinner from Soho restaurants or from parties in digs to dance to the music of such as Sidney Lipton and to quaff Scotch Ale or more exotic drinks served up by amateur barmen under Sid's command. After midnight, the formalities began to melt as the stiff white collars softened in the heat and we locals from 79 or 57 could slip in ticketless to the bar, exchange a pleasantry with Sid, and then wander around the dance floor in search of girls whose partners had inadvertently anaesthetized themselves. After the last waltz most of the lights would go out. Couples with no homes willing to receive them would sit or lie "snogging" on sofas that had been left strategically against the walls and some amateur would take over the Club piano and tinkle away in half-remembered pastiche of Art Tatum or Carroll Gibbons.

On such a night some tipsy joker slipped me a mickey in the form of a tumbler of gin to which he'd added a dash of orange squash. I was thirsty enough, and had drunk enough, not to notice and I knocked it back in one draught. Soon afterwards the floor started to tilt and jump up and hit me. Luckily Richard Brunel Hawes, known of course as "Bruno", the occupier of 57's first floor front, came to my assistance. He wasn't in much better shape than I was but he somehow managed to get me to

a lavatory and my head under the cold tap before we set out for home.

I remember us struggling through the fog. I was cold, pale and silent, clutching the railings for support. Bruno was hot, red and noisy, alternating curse with prayer as he tried to drag me along. When we got to 57 he somehow manoeuvred me upstairs and into my room, solicitously got me out of my clothes, into my pyjamas and into bed. I sank into immediate anaesthetized sleep which lasted till I was awakened by angry noises.

Bruno, it seems, had crept quietly from my bedroom and then, overwhelmed by his efforts, had sunk into deep sleep on the landing. The noise that woke me was Miss Lang's reaction to finding him when she arrived with the jugs of hot water.

"Now, now, Mr Hawes," she said. "That's hardly being the gentleman, is it? Why can't you behave like nice Mr O'Donnell there, quietly asleep in his bed."

In December the club lounge became an auditorium fitted
with rows of seats that faced the scaffolding stage on which we
performed the Christmas Show. It ran for ten nights and two
matinees and because few of the audience of some 5,000 would
understand private hospital jokes, it contained little incestuous
humour. Between 1949 and 1953 the cast was still, like the
Footlights, all male (though we had a female musical director),
and the show took the form of self-conscious "intimate revue"
with a lot of lolling about in dinner jackets and musical ac-
companiment from two pianos, double bass and drums. The
humour ranged from desperate attempts at *dégagé* sophisti-
cation to unashamed heartiness and most of it succeeded because we had an indulgent audience.

Thanks to my agreement with Allen Crockford, my involvement with the show was physically demanding. I spent about
three months writing it while trying to give the impression I
was doing some work in the hospital and making essential
cash-earning trips to the BBC Variety Department at Aeolian
Hall in Bond Street. We rehearsed nightly for about eight
weeks and then the stage crew and I spent a sleepless 48 hours
in lighting and technical rehearsals. Once we'd opened, we
finished off each performance with an all-night party for the
cast and carefully-selected members of the audience. Then
followed a morning's uneasy sleep, a bilious lunch, a listless
afternoon, and we were ready to repeat the cycle.

On one night during the run the show was followed by an
Old Boys' party at which the stars of yesteryear beguiled us
with the turns that had rocked 'em in the aisles in the twenties
and thirties. Most of the music came from Dr Alan Slater whose
only professional appointment at the time was that of gliding
correspondent to *The Times*. The last night party, which her-
alded the collapse of our exciting tinsel world, usually ended
in oblivion. I remember scaring my mother when, after my first
Christmas Show, I arrived home in Yorkshire, went straight
to bed and slept continuously for 48 hours.

The St Thomas's I knew deserved its reputation as a bastion
of conservatism. When I arrived students still spoke with pride
of the heroes of '48 who, on the night the NHS was born, painted
the embankment opposite the Houses of Parliament with the
slogan: "Boot out Bevan". I can remember only four students

who during the 1940 election acknowledged their allegiance to the Labour Party. And one of those was the son of a Labour MP. The oft-quoted paradox is that this reactionary institution produces a regular stream of radicals. Definers of the paradox usually quote the pre-war generations that produced the likes of Stephen Taylor, Denis Hill, Richard Doll, Tony Dornhorst and David Cargill. And while St Thomas's can proudly claim to have produced two government Ministers, both of them, Lord Taylor and David Owen, have been members of Labour governments. The paradox doesn't puzzle those of us who know that in our day there lurked behind the conservative façade as ill assorted a collection of talents as God, or Allen Crockford, could assemble. We were united only by our loyalty to an institution which, in turn, engendered loyalty to what I hope is still a liberal humanitarian profession.

We didn't allow clinical medicine to dominate our lives and we may not have learned enough medical science to satisfy the enthusiasts. But at least one consultant assured us there would be plenty of time for that after we qualified and, by then, we'd had a chance to learn other things which I don't want to define too closely or people will label them "vocational training" and start running courses in them. They included a disinclination to take ourselves too seriously, and other qualities I deem essential in a civilized society—and, oh, how that last phrase reveals my past membership of the Thameside academy.

I didn't know it in 1949 but my notion of part-time medical student, like that of a part-time doctor or a part-time anything else, was bang in the mainstream of St Thomas's tradition.

THE MEDICAL STUDENT GAME:
FORTY YEARS ON

I HAPPENED UPON a cruel piece of architectural design last week. I'd been dining with a bunch of other aging men. The wine had been good and there was lots of it, so for an hour or two we had the illusion we were indulging in highly spiced and witty conversation, that our minds had recaptured the zestful irreverence of youth, and that, all in all, we were a pretty sharp and sophisticated bunch.

Our hosts had sensibly hired a bus to return us to our hotel, and as I staggered down the bus steps I confronted the architectural discomfiter. The hotel wall in which the entrance doors were set was made of mirrored glass and suddenly this brittle, suave, and lively man-about-town came face to face with full frontal reality: a paunchy, balding, and bleary eyed old buffer in a rumpled dinner jacket. The effect was so salutary that I stood to one side and watched as each of my companions faced his personal image. Their reactions confirmed the commonplace assertion that an occasional vision of how we look to other people can be a sobering experience.

Two weeks before, at a parents' meeting at a Surrey school, I'd heard the careers master trying to help parents discover what sort of way their sons and daughters might make in the world. In the weary tones of a man reiterating a well-worn truth, he pointed out that only those who got the highest grades in A-levels stood any chance of becoming vets or doctors. Every year, he added ruefully, medical schools rejected unseen many of his pupils who he knew through long acquaintance had not just the intellectual ability to get a medical degree but also the human qualities that he, as a patient, thought were necessary in a doctor. He also saw the same schools accept students whom he thought unlikely to make good doctors—students who had little interest in medicine but had ambitious and competitive parents who wanted them to leap over every challenging academic hurdle. I've heard many schoolmasters and schoolmistresses express the same view. Just as I've heard medical school Deans express great satisfaction with their students. Indeed I'm impressed by the number of Deans who've repeatedly told me that their current bunch of students is the best they've ever had, suggesting there is a rising tide of excellence.

Doctors who teach in medical schools are less protective than Deans in their assessment of students and, over the past six or seven years, I have heard many of them criticize their school's admission policy and claim they see a growing number of students who they fear will not make "good doctors". This could mean, of course, that they and their Deans have different notions of what makes a "good doctor"; just as a well-informed patient like a schoolmaster may have yet another. I don't want them to standardize the game. I've always thought it healthy for our profession to have a loose interpretation of that dangerous adjective "good". But the criticism now coming from schoolmasters and schoolmistresses suggests that "good medical student" may indeed be being defined too narrowly, and the definition may lean too heavily on alphabetic precedence in A-levels.

One parent at the careers meeting I attended was a local doctor, much respected by his colleagues for his medical skills and much respected by his patients for being "a doctor you feel better for seeing". He had clearly been too busy practising medicine to notice how medical schools had changed their methods of selection and, when the careers master sat down, he confessed himself horrified. He suggested that a person does not need to be all that clever to be a doctor and indeed implied that a certain sort of cleverness—that which allows its possessor to progress too smoothly from bright sixth former to medical student, to houseman, to registrar, to consultant, to retirement, without too close an acquaintance with the hurly burly that lies outside the cloisters—could be a hazard to patients' happiness if not their health. In his book, indeed, health and happiness were much the same thing and he won warm applause from two other doctors who were present and even warmer applause from their patients.

I was one of the applauders. Most of the complaints I hear about doctors—and I mean complaints that seem well-founded and not just routine grouses—are not about the doctor's intellectual failing but about a lack of human qualities such as understanding or sympathy. I'm reactionary enough to think that some individuals are incapable of developing these qualities to the level that a doctor needs and I can't accept the notion that if students are bright enough you can correct that defect, and teach them, for instance, how to cope with people confronted by tragedy, by giving them instruction in Communication or Empathy.

Unless individuals have a real interest in the bizarre ways in which other people can live their lives, they may be impervious to training in certain human skills. To believe otherwise is to accept that Claudio Abbado can say to the leader of the London Symphony Orchestra: "We sound a bit thin on the strings these days, Charlie. Just nip down the pub, like a good boy, pick out a few likely lads, and we'll send them on a violin training course. Then, before you can say 'Thomas Beecham', we'll be back on top of the charts."

We who express our disquiet over the way modern Deans play the medical student game are sometimes accused of suggesting that high intellectual ability is incompatible with human feeling. The accusation is unfair. Indeed, in debates on "high technology medicine" I hear myself repeat, I suspect to the point of boredom, that the ability to use high technology, like the possession of high intelligence, is no bar to acting with kindness, sympathy, and understanding.

I am less dogmatic when I try to decide how clever a person needs to be to be a doctor. Clearly people need to be pretty bright to work in the front line laboratories of medical research, and clearly some medical jobs demand a higher level of intellectual ability than others, but what sort of cleverness is needed by those who are going to perform that mixture of clinical, administrative, and social tasks that is the eventual lot of most practising doctors?

A wise old BMA owl, David Bolt, once warned me against basing the answer to that question on standards that were acceptable 20 or 30 years ago. The scientific basis of medicine, he says, is advancing so rapidly that a doctor who is now an admirable GP might well be unsuitable for practice by the end of the century.

"To survive the training for medical qualification," he said, "demands a very high intellectual standard; to use effectively the methods of investigation now available requires no less."

His argument that students have to be bright to stay the course is, of course, self-fulfilling. Most criticism of methods of selection is also implicit criticism of the course. I carry a painful memory of a bright young doctor who told me he was leaving a practice that rendered useful service in a deprived area of a large city because he was wasting his medical training. Few of the patients who consulted him, he said, suffered from the conditions he had been trained to treat. Sadly, he couldn't see that his plight was open to alternative interpretation.

But what of Bolt's argument that the level of intellectual ability needed in everyday clinical practice needs to be high to keep pace with the scientific advance of medicine? Many doctors think otherwise. An orthopaedic surgeon in the North West (qualified sixteen years) claims that "high fliers" soon find everyday clinical practice too repetitive and boring; a consultant physician in the Midlands (qualified fifteen years) detects "growing disillusionment among young doctors when they discover that real medicine differs so much from the expectation generated during their training"; a GP in the South East (qualified five years) suggests that to survive in medicine you need not so much brain power as physical stamina and a damn good memory. Those are a typical few of the hundreds of criticisms I've heard aimed at the way the modern medical student game is being played.

When it comes to general practice, I have more direct evidence. For reasons of my own, I have recently spent some time "sitting in" on GP surgeries and my experience does not support Bolt's proposition. The main change I notice after a twenty year gap is that general practice has become a more civilized occupation—more civilized, that is for the doctors who now are given more time to think and to do their job properly, should they feel so inclined. Apart from that, I have to report that while the drugs have multiplied and the administrative procedures, not to mention the jargon, have grown more complex, most of the problems that patients bring to their GPs, and the useful responses the GP can make, are much the same as they were even 30 years ago. As one of the GPs who allowed me to "sit in" put it: "The repetitive mundanity of the medicine is just the same as it was when you were one of us. A GP can still maintain the intellectual challenge by pursuing a special interest, but what really keeps me going is the contact with the patients and my involvement in their lives."

Good GPs need, as they have always needed, to be well informed about the options that science has opened up for their patients, but my recent experience reinforces my reactionary view that the intellectual qualities I would deem essential in general practice are mental stamina—scientific advance hasn't relieved GPs of the need to make sensible decisions when under stress—and *nous*—which I would define as a blend of reasonable intelligence, commonsense, and the ability to learn from experience. I am unconvinced that high A-level grades give any indication of the existence of the second two-thirds of the *nous* triumvirate.

I'm delighted to report I'm not alone. I recently heard a British doctor claim that Israeli medical schools make all applicants take an IQ test and then reject anyone who scores too highly as being too clever to be a doctor. Potential medical students are selected from the middling to above average range and then have to take further personality tests. I hope he spoke the truth.

I've also heard a doctor criticize not just the grades demanded but the subjects. He is now a registrar in psychiatry, but was originally turned down by a medical school because he was foolish enough not to have decided on his future career at the grand old age of sixteen and wasted A-level time on subjects

like history and economics. Before he was acceptable, he had
to go back to school and read physics, a subject which he says
he has not had to use in the seven years since he qualified.

Deans and academic administrators hear these criticisms
often and use persuasive arguments when they defend their
policies to one another. But I wonder if they would be so
confidently persuasive if they had to step more often from the
comfortable bus and face the mirror on the wall.

Some trivial medical pursuits

THE PATRONAGE GAME

DEAR ALPHONSUS,

Your mother tells me you have at last outwitted the examiners and would like my advice on how to build a career in hospital medicine. You've already made the most important move by being born a man. Next you must acquire what we doctors call Authority. I've just seen a perfect example. An hour ago an old chum popped up on my television set. When we were students few would trust him with the price of a drink, and none with the address of a girlfriend. Yet there he was on my screen telling us why every twelve-year-old girl should or shouldn't be on the Pill; I forget which it was but he was very convincing.

Authority like that doesn't come cheap and you'll have to buy it by playing along with the system. Hospital jobs are less easy to come by than they once were but, if you get the protection of a well-ordered brotherhood around you, you'll find you can still progress through medicine without too much trauma —provided you keep your eyes down, your nose clean, and your thoughts and your flies buttoned up in public.

A good move is to get a job at one of those hospitals that call themselves "centres of excellence". Before you apply, find out what sort of person they're after: a "brain", a scrum half, a freemason, or even the occasional black or woman they're prepared to engage in these permissive times. Most likely they will be after a decent chap known to one of the consultants or recommended to him by another decent chap at another decent place. That's the job to go for, using all the arse-crawling ploys you picked up at medical school.

Once you're through the door, you yourself will become a decent chap and will remain one for evermore if you can cultivate a reputation for being "sound" and avoid the dreaded "too clever by half". You'll also get plenty of practice at the job because your boss is likely to be busy elsewhere; not necessarily ringing up the till in private practice but attending meetings where he can extend his acquaintance with men of influence and power. When Ian Aird was professor of surgery at the Royal Postgraduate Hospital, he used to travel a lot. When asked who did his work when he was away, he always replied: "The same people as do it when I'm here."

A centre of excellence will also afford you chances—in the corridors and wards, or over the coffee cups—to exchange well-turned witticisms or deep insightful remarks with some of medicine's most powerful patrons and to impress them, depending on which way you're aiming your career, with your modesty, your common sense, your zeal, or even your healthy irreverence (expressed, of course, only within decent limits). Don't underrate the value of these occasions because medicine's patrons have within their gift not just the best jobs but all the appurtenances that distinguish the gentlemen from the players.

If you're academically inclined, they can gain you access to research funds, consultancies to international agencies, and regular invitations to symposia in places like Florence, Tokyo, San Francisco, or Barbados. If you're keen to grub a living in private practice, they can arrange membership of dining clubs and appearance at postgraduate meetings, which get a man's name known within the trade—a much more effective way of attracting referrals of private patients than vulgar appearances in the public prints. And if you have a taste for pomp, the patrons can give you regular leg-ups on the beanstalk that has its roots in administrative and political committees and grows into the cloudborne land of gold chains, mutual votes of thanks, and even, whisper it softly, the reassuring touch of sword on shoulder.

Like all good Establishments, the system that distributes this patronage is not an organized network with a Mr Big skulking at its centre but an ill-defined scatter of well-meaning fellows, dropping a word here, a hint there, and earning each other's co-operation by lending support here, withdrawing it there. Indeed some are unaware of the power that they wield and take a naive delight in the success that seems to smile upon the decent young fellows whom they know.

Most doctors—they who enjoy their work—are amused by the antics of colleagues who play the patronage game. They mock rather than challenge and I suggest you follow their example. You may be irritated when you see the network perpetuating mediocrity, and when you see mediocre men, with nothing to defend but their unmerited authority, use patronage

to repel all intrusion by imagination, initiative or enterprise. But, whatever you do, don't speak out. Keep reminding yourself that Authority is all. Seek not to challenge it but to acquire it. Leave the grumbling to others, get on with your work, and don't get drawn into unpleasantness. If the going gets rough, just think hard about the index-linked pension that awaits you at the end of your comfortable amble.

Yours avuncularly,

THE TEACHING GAME

A MONTH OR two ago, I fell amongst a bunch of earnest souls eager to sharpen their skill as teachers or, as they preferred, "educationalists". They called their game a Creative Workshop —presumably to distinguish it from a knacker's yard or any other sort of destructive workshop—and many of the participants seemed to have stepped from a Posy Simmons cartoon. The event's most memorable feature was a kiosk labelled "Ethnic Sandwich Bar".

It was one of those occasions when ideas are acknowledged to emerge only from group activity, the notion that an individual might have a "good wheeze" being dangerously elitist, and I found myself attached to a "working group"—the repetitive titular use of "work" is another pathognomonic sign—which was to define desirable characteristics in a teacher.

Our suggestions were sought in creative kindergarten style. We were each given a bundle of colourful Magic Markers, had to write the two characteristics we thought most important on ragged pieces of brown paper, then walk to the front of the class and pin them to a piece of cardboard set on an easel. I thought hard about the teachers from whom I had learned my most valuable lessons, and then wrote "Enthusiasm" in fluorescent pink and "Imagination" in fluorescent green. In what I hoped would be seen as a "creative" gesture, I pinned "Enthusiasm" to the board upside down to draw attention to it. Only when I got back to my seat and looked at the gaudy display at the front of the class did I discover that my two suggestions stood out like a couple of jaundiced patients in a pale-faced ward. It wasn't a matter of colour but of vocabulary. My single words were surrounded by phrases like "workplace experience", "pedagogic authority" and "feedback sensitivity".

Our self-appointed leader, a fat man with beard and pebble glasses and clearly something of a denim fetishist, walked to the board, pointedly turned "Enthusiasm" the right way up and demanded a word with the perpetrator of the solecism. In an inspired moment I turned to the woman in the seat behind me, told her to own up and, in the confusion that followed, made my escape.

I've since discovered that this game is not the rare event I hoped it was and the fact that apparently sane people are prepared to play it is symptomatic of a sort of insecurity that afflicts some teachers—including some medical teachers. Recently I've had to attend a wide variety of events alleged to be concerned with medical education and to wade through some ill-written and pretentious "literature" on the subject. The experience prompts me to propose a couple of Laws of Educationalism.

The First Law runs: the greater the difficulty the lecturer has in keeping the audience awake, the more likely is the lecture to be about educational technique. The Second Law runs: the more opaque the prose, the more likely the article will include an exhortation to improve "communicative skills".

What I think I see happening is a phenomenon familiar in other trades such as acting and broadcasting. People who are not prepared to accept that insecurity is an essential ingredient of the job seek less hurtful reasons for explaining to themselves why others seem better able to engage the attention of an audience, to create the excitement that makes people want to know more, and to enthuse them to seek out knowledge for themselves. As it happens, I believe that a lot of people can acquire those skills but that the secret lies not in their trying to copy the technique of others but in their building upon their own individual quirks and characteristics. Learning to do this can be painful not just because it involves much agonizing introspection but because it means having to cope regularly with failure and rejection. Small wonder that many teachers seek to avoid it.

The easiest way to avoid it is to write off the personal qualities of others as irrelevant, to believe that anyone who has acquired the right knowledge, passed the right exams, and has a nodding acquaintance with the theory and jargon of "communication", is automatically endowed with the qualities of a teacher. Another way to sidestep the painful development of personal skills is to create an elaborate palisade of educational theory behind which insecure souls can reside, confident that they have acquired all the necessary attributes because they know how to set proper objectives, measure outcomes, and felt-tip the right words on creative brown paper.

Yet many teachers, who, while they are behind the palisade can convince us that they know exactly what their students need to be taught, succeed, when they actually get involved in the teaching, in boring their students into oblivion. Life would be harder for them if some mischievous person were to resurrect the suggestion made over 30 years ago by A. J. P. Taylor: "It would be no bad thing if academic promotion were open only to those who could hold listeners or win readers."

I remember a sleepy summer afternoon some 35 years ago when I sat amid a bunch of fellow medical students in an outpatients clinic at St Thomas's. Our teacher was the gynaecologist Joe Wrigley and he and we sat listening while a tense, rapidly-speaking woman gave us a minutely detailed account of her history of infertility with her own assessment of possible causes and the investigations she thought were needed. After she had left to go to the examination room, Joe turned to us and said in earthy Yorkshire tones: "I don't know, I don't know. These young women today seem to know more about the working of their genital apparatus than do I."

A serious-minded knowall in the front row, angered by this seemingly reactionary approach, piped up: "Surely what you're saying, sir, is that anxiety can be a major factor in infertility."

"Of course I am, lad," said Joe. "But I thought I was putting it more interestingly".

I suspect that doctors who play the teaching game under those rules find it more rewarding. I'm sure their students do.

THE ELECTRONIC WORDGAME

MEDICAL PUBLISHERS LAY great stress on neatness. Indeed, one of them recently said his "best authors" were those whose manuscripts had every page numbered, were neatly typed in double spacing, and free from spelling error. I felt quietly proud because in October 1982, virtually overnight, I clearly became a best author. These days, everything I write doesn't just earn top marks for neatness but is completely justified—not in a moral, social or economic sense, but in printers' jargon: the right hand margin is as neatly ruled as was the left.

Yet this miracle of presentation has been achieved, without benefit of secretary, by a writer whose early works consisted entirely of illegible prescriptions scribbled on a hand-held pad. That early clinical training ensured that when I took to less purposeful writing I was already a Biro man. I couldn't get on with a typewriter because I couldn't type fast enough to keep up with my thoughts. Nor could that ponderous mechanical device allow me to perform even the simplest manoeuvres of my trade: drawing arrows to link half paragraphs at the top of the page with quarter paragraphs at the bottom, differentiating between crossing out and half crossing out, inserting not just new sentences but ideas for new sentences to be written when my brain was clearer, or scrawling instructions to myself in the margin like: "Needs no adjective here. Try to think of wistful noun."

Typing lessons might have eased my problem but never would have solved it because I am an obsessional re-writer, working through ten or twelve versions of even the simplest pieces. Then, on that fateful October day, I discovered the microchip. I was making a film about computers in general practice and learned that a microcomputer fed with a word processing programme became a typewriter at which I could bash away as fast as I liked because I could correct any mistakes later. I could also use it to rewrite as often as I wanted—editing, chopping and changing just as quickly and more intelligibly than with a Biro. I tried my hand at other people's word processors, found a programme that suited me—for initiates, it's Wordstar—and bought my own.

Within a month I had become a dedicated microchip man and now am so conditioned that I find it difficult to write without one and rarely leave home without my "lap-held" machine that I can use on trains, on aeroplanes, in waiting-rooms and airport lounges. When I return to base I unload the words into my resident computer and subject them to that arduous process of hacking about known to romantic outsiders as "writing".

The home computer is ideal for one-man-bands like me: my saleable goods, my letters, and my invoices all come spewing out of the same machine. And for a writer, a word processor brings one unique delight.

The late Vincent Mulchrone described journalism as the only form of human activity that demands that the orgasm comes at the beginning. The excitement comes in getting the story or the idea and the tedious business of writing it is a sort of detumescence. The word processor, I'm delighted to report, restores the orgasm to its proper place in the order of excitement. When I've finished a few hours or days—or even weeks or months—of writing, re-writing, cutting, and reassembling until I'm almost satisfied, there comes a climactic moment when I press a button, the earth moves, and the teleprinter beside my desk starts to hammer out sheet after sheet of perfectly typed words at a speed unattainable by human hand.

At my time of life, such intensity of pleasure comes less often than it used to and I've got into the habit of delaying it. If the writing has taken a long time or involved more than the usual ration of sweat and despair, I don't dissipate it all in one quick jab at the button. When the machine is ready to run, I fix myself a drink, put something appropriate on the gramophone—usually Mozart but occasionally, if I've been writing for a learned journal, Wagner—settle in a comfortable chair and bide my time until harmony enwraps my soul. Then, and only then, do I allow my finger to caress the button.

I know that, like all workers in my trade, I look eagerly at new machines because, deep down, I'm seeking one that will write the damn stuff for me. What I'm really after is a computer into which I could enter instructions like: "The British Medical Journal: 1000 words. Subject: Whither arthritis? Style: Instructive but entertaining, rich but not gaudy." Then I would read a book, listen to music, or scratch my armpits until the screen

—I beg its pardon, visual display unit—announced it was ready for the orgasm.

The problem is that our medical journals were overcrowded long before the coming of the microchip and, somewhere amid their seamless pages of opaque prose, there still lie nuggets of information that busy doctors need but have no time to seek. What they need are not word processors that can write but ones that can read. Over to you, Sir Clive.

PRACTICAL TESTS

FOR ROMANTICS AND the light of heart, the month of June evokes memories of balmy evenings, of picnics by the river, of Wimbledon, and Glyndebourne. Yet when I dredge my adolescence and young adulthood for memories of June it keeps coming out as the month of The Exam.

When I was an undergraduate, medical students seemed to do many more exams than anyone else. We seem to have set a trend. Am I right in thinking that everyone now faces more exams than once they did or is my memory distorted by the fact that, as a family, we are revisiting O-level as our youngest sets off on the academic trail in pursuit of his elders? As I write, we're in the middle of the written papers and have already had most of the traditional events like the history question from the wrong period and the boy who turned up at the wrong time. Ahead lie the dreaded science practicals. I've tried to reassure the family that science practicals are a doddle, that they don't demand that you actually do anything *practical* like play the oboe or construct a wickerwork chair. But as usual the family assumes I'm merely offering doctorly (i.e. unjustified) reassurance.

Yet I'm sure I speak the truth. The "practicals" that studded my education rarely lived up to their title. The style was set by those botany exams in the pre-medical course. The options open to the examiners were so limited that, no matter how they dressed them up by instructing us to "Place Specimen A in Beaker B, cover it with water, and record your observations when heat is applied," we knew we were just boiling a piece of beetroot. And if you could remember what opened and closed the stomata on the surface of a leaf, you didn't need to look down your microscope to "Record your observations when specimen X is exposed to a) heat, b) light, and c) increased humidity." Indeed doing the experiment could be a drawback. If it went wrong and you were a truthful recorder, you'd probably lose marks. I've told our O-leveller that, if anything similar crops up next week, he should curb his curiosity, keep his eyes away from his microscope, and just record what should have happened.

Even as complex a subject as organic chemistry doesn't increase the examiners' scope. The first time I visited Cambridge I was still a schoolboy sent for testing to see if I had the makings of an undergraduate. The practical side of the exam involved preparing Substance Y and recording its melting point. The instructions for its preparation were so explicit that, if you couldn't guess what Y was, not to mention know its melting point, you shouldn't have been taking the exam in the first place. Yet the charade had to be played out. We had to pretend we didn't know what we were making and were judged presumably on the accuracy of our recorded melting point. We had three hours to do the job but, like most of the others, I prepared Substance Y with 90 minutes to spare. With time hanging heavy, I decided to try something I'd never done before—clean it up by recrystallizing it in benzine. It dissolved straight away and that was the last I saw of it. With only fifteen minutes to go, not one crystal of Y had re-appeared. I got so panicky that I tried to evaporate the benzine by heating the beaker with a bunsen burner and inevitably it caught fire. A kindly lab assistant smothered the flames with a spare gown before the examiner could spot them.

Having seen Cambridge and been bewitched by it, I wasn't going to yield my chance of getting there. I hid the blackened beaker in the bottom of a waste bin, got a bottle of something that looked like Substance Y off a shelf, poured a little pile of it on to a filter paper, and labelled it with what I knew was Y's melting point. At the time I felt my action verged on the criminal; now I see that I passed the only truly practical test in the exam.

Even those clinical exams that came later didn't demand a

practical *performance* from the examinee. They demanded luck. The enduring respect I had for the late Sir Hedley Atkins was born one afternoon when I sat staring gloomily at an array of pots containing pickled specimens. I was midway through my Surgical Finals and one of the tests was to examine the "pots" for fifteen minutes before answering questions about them. There were five I reckoned I had diagnosed and could say something about. But there were four that had me completely baffled. All I could do was to tilt the odds in my favour by placing the four rogues randomly among the others.

Hedley Atkins walked over from where he'd been questioning another unfortunate. "You've a lot of specimens there," he said. "Let's give a few of them to your neighbour." He examined my collection and then one at a time, and quite magically, he removed the four pots that would have sunk me.

On such ephemera, whole careers are built. I got through my Medical Finals with the help of a patient who had written a phonetic interpretation of phaeochromocytoma on a piece of paper because she couldn't pronounce it and a nice old boy who whispered: "Don't be too shy to stick your finger up my bum. They're paying me extra 'cos they say it's essential."

The only practical exam I know that earned its title was one my wife took ten years ago. For years she had worked as pianist and composer and, when she thought it might be fun to acquire some academic credentials, she had to start at the foot of the ladder. She enjoyed doing the early written exams sitting amid fourteen-year-olds but, with the coming of the practicals, the family began to feel the strain as the house resounded to repetitive performance of Beethoven's and Brahms's faster compositions. (Music practicals seem designed to test the ability to play a lot of notes quickly, rather than a few notes well.) Even our five-year-old got to know Beethoven's Opus 90 by heart and grew conditioned, whenever a wrong note erupted, to make the same reassuring noises that he himself received whenever he fell off his tricycle.

One night he knelt by his bed and prayed: "Dear God please make me a good boy and please help Mummy to get through her test. And, if you can't get her through, please ask the men to come and take away the piano." That June, if not this, he knew the meaning of a truly practical test.

Patients' games for doctors

ENGLAND'S FAVOURITE SYMPTOM

ROUND ABOUT THIS time last century, Dr Gustav Jaeger, professor of zoology at Stuttgart, published his book *Health Culture* in which he suggested that men and women would live healthier lives if they wore clothes made entirely of animal hair and, in particular, of wool. An English philanthropist, Lewis Tomalin, was so enthused by Jaeger's ideas that he translated the book and published it in England at his own expense. *The Times* weighed in with a leader supporting Dr Jaeger's proposition and Tomalin, as a philanthropic gesture, opened a shop with a sign above its door that read: "Dr Jaeger's Sanitary Woollen System".

The healthy dressing game was played by such as Oscar Wilde and George Bernard Shaw who walked about London in some of the first Jaeger suits but it took Tomalin five years to realize that his private obsession had the makings of commercial success. He became a full-time businessman and opened the string of shops which has since grown into the international Jaeger business. The tale has an engaging English dottiness about it and is well worth its place in Godfrey Smith's *The English Companion*. This "Idiosyncratic A–Z of England and Englishness" is a compulsive and amusing read yet is barren of entries referring to one form of human activity. Search as you may through the index, you will find no reference to health or medicine, nurses, doctors or patients.

Apart from the "Sanitary Woollen System", the nearest Smith gets to our territory is an anatomical celebration of the round, honest, and unambiguous word which Englishmen use to describe the human fundament. Americans, he complains, use a niminy-piminy word that can also mean donkey. (The problem could be one of pronunciation. Bath, for instance, is a city that many Americans wish to visit but never can pronounce, and I once ran into trouble on the other side of the Atlantic when telling the tale of the ingenious fellow who tricked the pre-war *Daily Mail*, notorious for its topsy-turvy views, into publishing a letter signed "R. Supwards".)

A friend of Smith challenged me to invent a suitable medical entry for the book and, without much hesitation, I suggested: "Bowels, pride in control over". Few doctors have escaped the proud Englishman who, no matter how depressed he may seem during a consultation, will respond to the diffident inquiry "Bowels?" with a sunburst of triumphant smile and a defiant: "Regular as clockwork, Doc."

I was reminded of this source of national pride a few months back when listening to *The World At One*. The BBC correspondent was describing trouble in the streets of Teheran and though, in truth, he was underestimating the power of a transitive verb used intransitively, he sounded as if he were describing an admirable example of British stoicism. "Although the situation is stressful," he said, "British citizens have been advised not to evacuate." He then compounded his syntactical offence—and enhanced our chauvinistic pride—by adding: "The French have already evacuated and the Germans are threatening to do so."

Until the Second World War, the British bowel culture was dominantly a middle-class phenomenon. But after the war, it spread rapidly through the lower orders, carried by returning soldiers who had learned its glories from such officers as Apthorpe in Evelyn Waugh's *Men at Arms* who travelled with his personal thunderbox.

A neat description of middle-class bowel worship can be found in a 1939 revue sketch by Herbert Farjeon, in which a puffy, overblown, complacent widow—played originally by Hermione Baddeley—sits amid the palms and wicker of a hotel "sun lounge" in Torquay, a town she visits each winter because "it is less costive than Bournemouth, don't you find?" When an elderly colonel tries to reminisce about his "chronic condition" she interrupts: "Mine was naturally, acute. And as sudden as *that*. (She snaps her fingers.) "Sir Wilfred Hacker—such an able man—assured me afterwards that, had he operated five minutes later, I should never have seen the inside of a nursing home again.

"I was perfectly all right on the Monday. I was perfectly all right on the Tuesday. I was perfectly all right on the Wednesday. On the Thursday I got up—*perfectly* all right—had my breakfast—passed the morning—had my lunch—just a little soup, a grilled sole, a soufflé—passed the afternoon—had my tea—just an ordinary plain tea—not a *qualm*. And within five minutes I was writhing on the hearthrug like an eel."

And at this point, I'm reliably informed, the thirties audience having read the innuendo, and recognized the obsession, was huddled together in defensive laughter. Yet I'm sure those well-bred ladies of uncertain age whom the two Hermiones—Gingold and Baddeley—continued to play well into the 1950s would have admitted no other form of physiological discussion to their drawing rooms. Bowels, pride in control over, was an exception.

I suspect this bit of "Englishness" came, as did so many, from the public schools. Certainly, every morning at my prep school, we had to pass in line before the matron who barked at each of us: "Been?" and those foolish enough to answer "No" were dosed with a foul tasting draught which I now suspect was a mixture of rhubarb and senna. Even those of us who were streetwise and always responded "Yes, matron" got to know the taste of the stuff because it was her universal panacea. Anyone confined to the infirmary, be it with a sore throat, German measles, or a bruised toe, had to consume a morning dose. My class was lucky in that one of our number didn't seem to mind the taste and would swallow anyone else's on the payment of two sweets. I remember one morning, during the great chicken-pox epidemic, when he actually consumed nine doses. He now produces party political programmes. It's reassuring to remember that, at least, he has the stomach for the job.

DANGEROUS EXERCISE

SPORT THREATENS NATION'S health says doctor ... to be precise, says this doctor.

By sport, I don't mean the inconsequential activities we once called games. Nor that fifties dream of underprivileged youth earning health through joy on Duke of Edinburgh playing fields. I mean the aggressive, humourless, track-suited, custombooted activities that fill the back pages of tabloid newspapers and the front pages of television schedules.

This evening, on my television set, I saw yet another act of gratuitous violence on a football field. The victim was taken off on a stretcher to be sewn up by a surgeon. The aggressor explained it was "a man's game". His manager said it had been "a little bit physical". The referee, who'd been quick to penalize anyone who affronted his dignity, didn't even give a free kick. The commentator commended him for doing "a sound job". Maybe soccer has become a substitute for war and, as such, it is preferable to the real thing. But we need to acknowledge the unhealth it generates around it.

I'm surprised no sociologist has suggested that soccer hooligans are imitating the violence they see not on the pitch but in the boardroom. There the "win at any price" policy is pursued even more ruthlessly than on the field ... or on the terraces. The few times I've been favoured with the post-match gin and tonics, the air has been thick with those phrases beloved of "marketing men" who like to show off their aggressive amorality: "Nice guys come last", "Blessed are the meek, for they shall make way for the ruthless."

Sport catches 'em young. Thirty years ago one of the pleasures that went with walking my dog through Battersea Park was watching seven- and eight-year-old schoolboys playing football. One boy stood between each set of goalposts, blowing on his fingers and shouting, "Please sir, can I come out now sir?" and the other twenty chased the ball around the field in a joyful pack like a boxful of clockwork toys that had been wound up and poured on to the pitch. Even the master who did the refereeing seemed to enjoy himself.

A few weeks ago, I walked past the same pitch. The boys were no larger but were clearly engaged in a sterner activity than that I witnessed 30 years ago. There were no laughs, few smiles, and certainly no free-for-all chases after the ball. On the touch line stood three track-suited masters shouting the aggressive clichés of our time: "Get stuck in", "Put yourself about", "Make your presence felt". The boys showed they knew what was expected of them as they kicked and tripped and agonized but, to my jaundiced old eyes, they seemed to be having a lot less fun than I'd seen their fathers have on the same patch of mud and grass. But then my jaundiced old eyes have to cope with a lot these days: cricketers fighting with spectators, Wimbledon pretending to offer tennis but selling the thrills (important word that) that used to draw people to bullfights.

Then there are the headlines: "England . . . shame . . . disgrace . . . triumph . . . horror . . . vanquished". The language is the language of a war correspondent. This, I admit, is not sport but showbusiness. The damage comes when the attitudes drift down into the games that people play to have fun or because we doctors have persuaded them that the activity could be healthy.

On the local tennis courts where, when I played, the game included all sorts of activities unknown at Wimbledon—such as the regular ceremony of counting the balls—a fracas broke out last summer and the police had to be called when two players started assaulting one another over a disputed line call.

But then Sport isn't meant to be fun. I mean, it's all about winning, isn't it David?

Even as gentle a game as cricket can be turned into Sport if you inject the players with "needle". And what about Rugby Union which prides itself on being a player's game? Once it becomes Sport, it loses the restraint that once kept players from using the abundant opportunities it provides for aggressive violence. I gather I'm not the only middle-aged spectator to think that international rugby now includes too much cynical thuggery. Yet, such is people's loyalty to the game, they don't like to let the side down by admitting how far Sport has invaded their amateur territory. Even as gentle a man as the commentator Bill McClaren is drawn into the conspiracy, disguising the evidence of his own eyes with euphemism.

I've compiled a McClaren glossary. "Use of the foot" means

kicking an opponent. "Dangerous use of the foot" means kicking an opponent in the teeth. "Dangerous use of the boot" means stamping hard on an opponent's genitals. That use of the definite article—as if The Foot were a piece of equipment handed to the players before the game—puts a disinfectant barrier between the incident and its description.

Not only do we accept the New Aggression. We erect monuments to it. The least leisurely acre near where I live is a large redbrick building ostentatiously called a Leisure Centre. When I eavesdrop on its dressing-rooms, I hear little talk of having fun but much discussion of how to get "psyched up". Small wonder that the games themselves, from squash to five-a-side football, are heavily beset with accusations of cheating, actual cheating, and angry and aggressive exchanges between the players. I don't think our local sportspersons are more cruel, greedy, or discourteous than others. Their attitudes, like their track-suits, come off the same production line. All of us now know that the only object of Sport is to win. I mean that's what it's all about, isn't it Brian?

I indulge this grouch not because I hanker for times past—though I do—nor because my attitude to sport is unashamedly middle-class—though it is. I indulge it as a doctor because I object to people justifying this celebration of aggression by claiming it is healthy—and I'm damn sure that it isn't. It engenders unhealthy mental attitudes and encourages unhealthy physical behaviour. And any doctors who encourage it are themselves playing a dangerous game. Modern sport is a patients' game that doctors should leave well alone.

Throughout history, burly aggressors who have tortured, maimed and murdered the meek, have prided themselves on their physical condition and their will to win. They may have been physically fit but please don't let's say that they were healthy.

THE IMPORTANCE OF BEING PARANOID

PROFESSIONAL WISEACRES, lyricists of popular songs, agony aunts, folksy comedians, and other popular psychotherapists,

are never slow to remind us just how much we need friends.
Fewer people bother to remind us just how much we need
enemies. Yet I wonder how many of us could determine our
identities without a fantasy Them—or even a real Them—
whose ineptitude, stupidity, ignorance and sloth allow us to
perceive ourselves as the bright, industrious persons that we
know we are; a Them whose capacity for evil doing makes
us, if not wholly free from human frailty, at least persons of
genuinely honest intent. Some people seem to draw all their
energy and creative drive from their long and unyielding
struggle against Them. And I am not thinking of people who
are mentally ill. To borrow an image from the woman who
announced that she was "slightly pregnant", maybe we underrate the importance of being "slightly paranoid".

Our need for this healthy sub-paranoia is so great we usually
incorporate a sound, reliable enemy in our human institutions.
Government and Opposition establish their identities largely
in terms of their opponents' alleged inadequacies. "I admit
we've made a slight nonsense of this but, Ya Boo, look what
you did when you were in power." And where would political
parties be without their enemies? How could they manage
without Tony Benn, Arthur Scargill, or Mrs Thatcher? If such
persons didn't exist, their opponents would have to invent them.
Maybe they did. Even one-party governments have to create
"dissident elements" to blame when the trains don't run on
time, when the crops fail, or when they need to lock someone
up to remind the people that it is healthier to listen to official
truth than to aberrant fancy.

A visiting Martian would hear evidence of enemy infiltration
in many of our social exchanges.

"Of course, They would like us to think that They are very
busy in Head Office."

"When I took in those copies Karen and I had been checking
all day, guess what They said? We can't have them back until
Tuesday. But when Mr Carter comes down and starts creating,
who's going to get the blame? . . . not Them, for sure."

"Did you see that dreadful rubbish They put on the television
last night?"

Doctors seem to have picked up the sub-paranoia game
from their patients and have become eager players. It's

extraordinary how many of them choose to define the success of their work in terms of others' failure. Achievement always burns brighter when the fuel is Their inadequacy.

When I was a student, the enemy was billeted at St Elsewhere's and the cheeriest players of the sub-paranoid game were the orthopaedic surgeons. As we watched them treating a patient in the Fracture Clinic, they would tell us: "If this poor chap had been less fortunate he would have gone to St Elsewhere's where They would have coated him with plaster and put him on his back for weeks. Here we'll have him walking round the ward by Tuesday."

And when the urologists started to use a new operation that made the removal of a prostate a less messy business than it used to be, they didn't say: "Look how clever we are. We've learned a new technique." Instead we heard: "If this poor man had gone to St Elsewhere's, They would have subjected him to rubber tubes, glass jars, and a permanent uriniferous aroma. Here we'll have him peeing like a horse by Thursday."

A lot of medical teachers still like to project themselves as crusaders. But to become a credible crusader you need to create a few credible infidels. And that is where They, the inhabitants of St Elsewhere's, get dragged in. Once They are identified, the fight is always fun and often profitable; one of the most valuable reputations to have in private practice is that of someone who cures Their incurables.

Doctors eager to become crusaders must beware of going over the top. The ideal identity is not that of a true heretic but that of an altogether more reassuring soul, the "bit of a heretic". Medicine being what it is, yesterday's heresy all too often becomes today's received truth. Then the wise warrior, he who didn't go over the top, can sheathè his sword and enjoy his reward. As a profession we tend to treat yesterday's crusaders with respect, even load them with an honour or two.

Because we learn the sub-paranoia game in our medical schools when we are at an impressionable age, we never forget it. And, as we fight the good fight against disease and ignorance, we discover other enemies worthy of our steel. For many a hospital doctor the enemy is The Administrator; for a few GPs, the enemy, sadly, is their patients. But for most doctors the common enemy is the bad doctor who works elsewhere and

whose low clinical and ethical standards are our only measure
of the excellence of our own.

Our patients, we know, are treated by wise, knowledgeable,
and kindly doctors, aware of their ethical responsibilities, conscious that each patient is not a mere collection of symptoms
but an individual enmeshed in an interconnecting social network etc. etc. Other less fortunate patients are treated by Them.

HUMAN SPECTACLES

I NEVER KNOW quite what sort of stroke to play when someone
whom I like, whose professional skill I respect, and who renders
me useful service, bowls me a political opinion with which he
assumes I sympathize but with which I profoundly disagree.
Judging whether to play it off the back foot or the front can be
a delicate decision, particularly if the service you require is
being rendered at the time, even more particularly if the render-
ing of it puts you at a disadvantage and you are tipped back-
wards in a dentist's or a barber's chair. I usually respond with
a dull defensive block, a grunting noise that most bowlers
interpret as an indication of agreement. I ran into a variation
of this game recently when I visited a dispensing optician and
was preached a sermon of complaint about the government's
expressed intention to "deregulate" the selling of spectacles.

As it happens, I'm all in favour of people being able to buy
glasses, as they do in the United States, by rummaging through
assorted spectacles on a shop counter until they find a pair that
suits. Yet I could see that if I didn't grunt pretty smartly last
month, my friendly neighbourhood optician would likely jump
up and down on the new lenses he was polishing with such
angry vigour. Luckily, he saved me from shameful deception
with the sentence with which he finished his tirade. "I didn't
expect that of Norman Fowler," he said. "I always thought
he was one of us." What an interesting observation, I
thought. Norman F. does look like an optician; perhaps we
should be told.

Then I realized I'd misunderstood. The angry lens polisher
clearly included me in the "us" and I wondered which of the

oppressed minority groups of which I'm a diligent member he
had in mind. When it dawned on me which "us" he meant, I
found he'd presented me with the means of avoiding a direct
political response. "You're making a terrible mistake," I said.
"Norman Fowler isn't one of us."

"Yes, he is," he said. "I've seen him wearing them on television."

"That doesn't make him one of us," says I, eager to flush
misapprehension from his mind. "Lots of people wear spectacles
on television but that doesn't make them true glasses wearers.
Maybe I haven't seen Norman F. without his glasses but I *think*
I have and I certainly know what he looks like without them.
You can't say that of a real glasses wearer. Real wearers'
spectacles become so much part of them that not even Leonardo
could conjure up a vision of what their faces might look like
without them.

"Take that former BMA secretary, Lord Hill," says I, according the poor man one of his lesser distinctions but one I felt sure
would impress an optician. "My mind can't create a believable
memory of his face without including glasses. And how about
Denis Norden?"

Here maybe I was on surer ground.

"I can't even begin to imagine what he looks like without
glasses. Those glasses are part of the essential Norden. Perhaps
he takes them off when he goes to bed at night but I wouldn't
be surprised to learn he has to remove them with a surgical
instrument."

I remembered my optician was a Durham lad. "Once upon a
time you may recall," I said, "*What the Papers Say* was presented by an editor of the *Northern Echo* called Harold Evans
who wore a pair of practical no-nonsense Northern specs. It
puzzles me why people confuse him with an altogether different
non-spectacled person of the same name who later appeared as
editor of the *Sunday Times*. I doubt that they're even related.
Evans is a common name."

My optician explained that, although he agreed they didn't
look alike, he had it on good authority they were the same man.
Indeed by the time he'd finished telling me what his sister's
husband thought about that nasty Mr Murdoch and what he'd
done to nice Mr Evans, he'd quite forgotten about deregulation

and I was able to have my new frames fitted in a calm apolitical atmosphere.

Yet, in my desperate search for a diversion, I think I may have latched on to something real. Most people in their late forties acquire spectacles, if only for reading. But, at that age, they can put them on and take them off as if they were a cosmetic. Your true specs wearer is one who started with pre-pubertal wire frames and who survived adolescence despite an affliction which, for my generation anyway, was even more of a handicap than acne. Most of us boys were called "specky foureyes" long before we got out of short pants, and many young women refused to wear their glasses in public, particularly if they were out with a boyfriend. Many got labelled as "stuck up" because they didn't acknowledge people they knew in the streets and I know of one woman who now gets enormous pleasure from television re-runs of films she thought she would have enjoyed when she first heard them in a cinema, though she never saw them clearly because she was always with a boyfriend.

That early suffering turned us into chauvinists who now acknowledge as comrades only persons who have the prosthesis built into their personality. We resent being classified with frivolous wearers of glasses like politicians who use them for waving around, for chewing the ends of, or for snatching off to make dramatic gestures. Just as we resent those academics who acquire glasses because they think they can look wise or eccentric by peering over a pair of heavy frames perched on the tips of their noses. And as for those unspeakable persons who wear spectacles dangling from a string around their neck . . . dammit all, it's an integral part of our anatomy that they're trivializing.

Yet, though we despise trivializers, we have great sympathy for genuine specs wearers who defect and acquire contact lenses. Indeed, there is talk of our setting up a counselling service of caring glasses-wearing persons to give ongoing support to colleagues who "come out" too abruptly from behind their frames and are unprepared for the abrupt change of personality that it entails. In a just society, these victims of our time would be able to treat acute attacks of identity crisis by dashing into the nearest Woolworths to grab a pair of specs from the counter and instantly recreate a familiar and comfortable persona. That's why some of us regard deregulation of the sale of glasses as not just sensible but humane.

The cruellest blow many of us have suffered recently was a headline in the *Guardian*: "Spectacles sex myth shattered". In a Gallup survey, we were told, "overwhelming percentages" of interviewees had said that spectacles were unimportant in the sexual appeal of men and women. The news came 40 years too late to exorcize the horrors of my adolescence. Typical, I might say, of the treatment dished out to those for whom spectacles are, as near as dammit, a congenital affliction.

Doctors' games for patients

HOUSEHOLDER'S PARANOIA

ONE OF THE few under-reported hazards of twentieth-century living is Householder's Paranoia. When I was a GP, I soon discovered that it isn't big things that prey most on people's minds: the Bomb, industrial anarchy, the impending collapse of civilization as my next door neighbours know it. These are threats that people learn to live with. The greatest provokers of anxiety and fear are small things. And the greatest—or smallest—of these is Householder's Paranoia. Its aetiology is fully documented in the top left hand drawer of our kitchen dresser where we keep the instruction manuals that have come with the high technology domestic appliances we've admitted to our home—indeed, not just admitted but greeted with the sort of enthusiasm with which the Trojans welcomed their gift horse.

Maybe I harbour too great a respect for experts, but if people devise a dishwasher, a lawnmower, a motor car, or a ratchet screwdriver, and choose to issue an instruction manual with it, I assume they know what they are doing. If the manual says the car owner should check the radiator level every day, and the tyre pressures and battery level every week, then that's what an obsessional creature like me will feel obliged to do.

In the early days, the obligatory routines can be refreshing —an opportunity indeed to give outward sign of the inner pride of ownership. When I got my first car, for instance, never were wiper blades more solicitously examined, never was chrome more lovingly lathered ("Use only soap and warm water", said the manual in a paragraph that implied that using polish was the sin that dare not speak its name), never were tyre treads more assiduously inspected. And I revelled in the challenge to keep our first lawnmower in fighting trim. Adjusting the height of the cut, adjusting the spark-plug gap, cleaning the rollers, even draining the sump, were all tasks I tackled with the quiet enthusiasm of someone who cared. The obsessional burden grew as, deluded that we were making life easier for ourselves, we acquired more household mechanicals with joints to be greased, nuts to be adjusted, filters replaced, and vulnerable parts to be protected from rust.

There was no room for compromise. The manuals were brutally frank about the consequences of neglect. I doubted we could survive the shame if our lawnmower seized up on the front lawn or if killer rust ate into the vitals of our car and released a cascade of ball bearings all over our high class residential road. The tyranny of maintenance began to take over my leisure and even interfere with my work. And it wasn't only machines. Often, of a spring evening, I would flop into an armchair exhausted from my ritual tasks like cleaning the cassette recorder's heads, capstan, and pinch roller, the six-weekly adjustment of the agitator brushes in the carpet cleaner, the essential monthly check on the operating temperature of the yogurt maker, the statutory weekly debridement of the crumb tray under the toaster (I wonder how many of you have read that piece of small print), only to see Percy Thrower pop up on my television to inquire why I wasn't out in the garden pricking out my delphiniums.

It was the garden that brought my neurosis to its *crise*. Some well meaning person gave me a book entitled *Your Garden Day by Day* which listed rewarding things for amateur gardeners to do on every damned day of the year. I glanced through it and felt extremely ill.

I was to start the year, as I recall, by mulching my asparagus, sowing my shorthorn carrots on a hotbed, and forcing my rhubarb. Come the spring, when younger men's fancy might turn to thoughts that some of us never wholly abandon during the winter, mine would be directed towards pruning my forsythia, thinning my hardy annuals, and spraying my gooseberries. While others lay in summer shade, listening to the chock of leather upon willow, I would be busy stopping my carnations, pricking off my primulas, and syringing my runner beans. And when December came and jovial men sat beside roaring fires supping mulled wine, guess who would be the lonely figure out there in the gloom protecting his celery and pruning his Clematis jackmanii.

That book had one glaring omission. Search as I might, I could find no time off, no day allocated to just sitting in the garden and enjoying it. That omission was therapeutic for it led me to coin the dictim by which I have since lived: "If you can't do a job properly, don't do it at all." I now accept that all household mechanicals are disposable and, if needs be, replaceable when they expire from maintenance starvation. I've also done no gardening, save for an occasional spell of lawnmower guiding, and I don't feel at all deprived because I enjoy watching others. Indeed, the greatest reward that gardening can offer comes to the man who settles comfortably in a deck chair, favourite drink in hand, and watches his wife silhouetted against a fine sunset hacking her way through a thick patch of nettles.

True contentment comes only to those who shed their burden of obsession and discover one of life's central secrets: that a well-rounded being is one who has cultivated a few redeeming defects. Each year of self-denial makes it easier to fight off temptation and the last time spring sunshine danced upon the implements in our local garden centre, I found it but the work of a moment to renew my resolve to remain a free man.

We achieve maturity, I've decided, when we discover that although striving after perfection has some place in our lives —when we're at our work or at our prayers—it has no place at all in our homes.

QUID PRO QUO

THERE IS ONE form of human contact even more hedged about with moral and emotional insecurity than the doctor-patient relationship. It is, of course, the doctor-bankmanager relationship. By calling it a relationship, doctors can pretend it isn't really a game when in truth it is often the most challenging encounter in the medical sporting calender. The fashion these days is to clothe relationships with adjectives plucked from the lexicon of sociology—meaningful, ongoing, that nature of thing. To describe the ideal liaison between GP and bankmanager we need to turn to humbler biological texts. *L'adjectif juste*, I suggest, is symbiotic.

My grounds for thinking so are eight contented years I spent in symbiotic rapport with our Mr Crowfoot at the National Provincial. In those days the manager's office was a compartment at the back of the bank, screened from observation from the counter by a glass partition rendered opaque by frosted tracery. Mr Crowfoot clearly had a peephole because, whenever I entered the bank and he was not engaged with another customer, he would open his door and beckon. "Could I have a quick word, doctor?" The first time it happened, I was terrified. I had a vision of my wife and baby perched on a sofa in the road outside our house surrounded by our pathetic worldly goods, just like the other unfortunates who were turfed into the streets for indulging in my kind of fecklessness. Mr Crowfoot must have sensed my worry for he immediately put my mind at ease by slipping into the routine that later was to follow every request for a quick word.

He closed the door, flopped into his chair, and placed the palms of both hands over his epigastrium. "You see it starts here, doctor, and then moves slowly downwards until suddenly, just like that, it goes stab, stab, stab, like a red hot blade going in and out, in and out. Then after the stabbing comes the churning and that feeling that there's a demonic creature in there struggling to get out."

Normally a gentle unassuming man, Mr Crowfoot was able to draw on unsuspected reserves of vocabulary and emotional intensity when he described symptoms. After half a dozen visits to his office, I had established that he had two principal afflictions: the red hot blade in the belly and the excruciating pressure on the top of the head. Yet on those humble foundations he could build a symptomatological Byzantium.

I had also learned that the only response that the game expected of me was that I should listen. I once, foolishly, sent Mr Crowfoot for a barium meal but all that did was provide a source of more exotic symptoms attributable to "those x-rays".

The poor man was beset by much anxiety and, in the early days of our liaison, I listened not just with the simulated sympathy in which we doctors occasionally indulge but with a genuine pity because I was sure my own financial misdoings played a part in the aetiology.

It was some time before I appreciated the *quid* I was getting

pro quo. Though I was a regular visitor to Mr Crowfoot's office, not once did he raise the delicate matter of the pressure that my account must be putting on the bank's reserves. Nor did bank charges appear on my statement. And when, one day, I asked him for an overdraft, he granted it immediately and with a smile.

"Don't you want some collateral?" I asked, showing off a word I'd read on the City pages.

"The only security I need, doctor, is my knowledge of you as a customer. I know my customers in the same way that you know your patients. I back my own judgement. And, by the way, last night it wasn't so much pressure on top of the head as a band of steel around the brow twisted tighter and tighter by a medieval torturer . . ."

Our game relationship grew so solid that one morning I played a variation. Mr Crowfoot came to my consulting room and, as he settled in the seat beside my desk but before he'd drawn breath to intone his symptoms, I asked for and received a modest loan for the purchase of a petrol-driven lawnmower. I never repeated the manoeuvre. It was nice to prove that the game could accommodate it but I had no wish to disturb the harmony of our relationship.

Mr Crowfoot came from the same tradition as Mr Beckley, manager of the National Provincial at the end of Westminster Bridge, whose generous bonhomie and ability to cast a blind eye in every direction, ensured the financial survival of generations of St Thomas's Hospital medical students. Yet he too was playing the quid pro quo. Far from acting recklessly with the bank's money, he was acting shrewdly, engendering a loyalty to the National Provincial in customers who had a reasonable chance of later becoming solvent. When he retired, the hospital gave him a send-off more extravagant than that accorded Florence Nightingale.

He and Mr Crowfoot have long since passed beyond the great glass partition in the sky—or was it to a bungalow in Peacehaven?—but they represented a species that now appears to be extinct. Their banks were homely places that echoed the tenor of the homely corporate name, the National Provincial. When it became the Natwest, the Crowfoots and Beckleys were replaced by persons who specialized in "marketing" and "systems analysis" games rather than the good old quid pro quo. I fell out with them when they tried to get me to take a hand in a Blame the Computer game, telling me their electronic marvel couldn't transfer money automatically from one account to another. This meant I had to pay them hefty charges for the privilege of borrowing my own money and I could find no wise old cove like Mr Crowfoot or Mr Beckley to whom I could appeal.

I have since freed myself from that absurdity and, of an evening, play my own computer game, transacting my financial business down the wires to the Homelink service of the Nottingham Building Society and the Bank of Scotland, whose names I find as comforting as the old National Provincial.

In response to my defection, I got a letter from the person who occupies Mr Crowfoot's old chair—now fashioned, I suspect, from chrome and leather rather than from mahogany and moquette. Enclosed with the letter was a leaflet that explained that the old emporium has taken to calling itself, may God forgive it, "The Action Bank".

A slick public-relations phrase seems a poor foundation for a mutually profitable relationship, at least when compared with a manager with waterbrash.

WHICH END OF THE STETHOSCOPE?

I'VE NEVER QUITE mastered the doctor-patient game. From the patient's side of the net, that is.

The first time I felt a compelling urge to play the game was the night I discovered I was dying. I was a second-year clinical student at the time and, because I was also working as scriptwriter in the BBC's variety department, I'd mastered the details of only the funnier diseases. I knew enough, however, to share my generation's fear of phthisis.

One evening, after I'd lit my fifty-second cigarette of the day, I gave a nasty hawk and produced a gobbet of genuinely blood-stained sputum. I knew at once I'd been invaded by tubercle bacilli because I'd seen *A Song to Remember* in which Cornel Wilde, as Chopin, spattered regular technicolored haemoptyses over the ivory keys.

Prompted by that Hollywood memory, I decided to face up bravely to the inevitable. How long had I got? Months rather than years I suspected, and perhaps only weeks. In those days, streptomycin was not even a twinkle in a chest physician's eye. In my dingy Victorian room across the road from the hospital, I sat beneath a purring gas mantle and reviewed the achievements of a promising young life. It didn't take long.

Next I decided that, before I handed myself over to the doctors, I'd best try to put my affairs in order. I composed a rather touching letter to my parents thanking them for their love and for their moral and financial support, and apologizing for the pain that my many acts of waywardness must have caused them. In retrospect I can see I made the apology a touch over-poignant but I suspect I was still under the influence of Cornel Wilde. Then I drafted a list of bequests to ensure that my closest friends would receive my most treasured possessions: my Superstar hockey boots, my virgin Gray's Anatomy (untouched by hand), my signed photograph of Ingrid Bergman, and my framed exhortation, purloined from a golf club dressing-room: *Will members please refrain from washing their balls in the basin.*

I guessed that, at my age, Proust would have been able to assemble more significant symbols of times past but the hour was too late for me to rustle up any literary garnish. And it didn't really matter because, once I'd disposed of these trappings of a past life, a great calm entered my soul. I picked up the frugal parcel I needed for my last journey—my sponge bag and slippers wrapped in my pyjamas—and, as I walked to the pillar box to post my letter to my parents and then through the hospital portico for the last time, my spirit rode the crest of a soaring Puccinian melody.

My re-ordering of my affairs had taken some time and it was one o'clock in the morning when I walked into Casualty. The only doctor allowed to examine students was the Resident Assistant Physician (RAP), more senior than a senior registrar and really a consultant-in-waiting. It never crossed my mind he might be irked at having to rise from his bed to minister to a dying man. He wore a white coat over his pyjamas and seemed unimpressed as I unfolded my dramatic tale. Indeed, he rudely interrupted it, ordered me to open my mouth, and brusquely flattened my tongue with a wooden spatula. Then he announced that I'd abraded a small blood vessel at the back of my throat and shooed me off to the room I thought I'd never see again.

I remember no feeling of relief. I'd grown rather fond of the idea of a romantic exit. All that sympathy I'd counted on receiving as one so young fighting so bravely and uncomplainingly had been dismissed in one short snarl from the RAP. And my father never let me forget the more abject paragraphs of my letter.

Since then I don't think I've got any better at playing the patient game. Luckily I have a GP who appreciates that wild fantasies are prone to wander in my brain and he treats me with a reassuringly firm hand. But I have yet to master my relationship with consultants. They're always considerate and kind but, maybe because I write for the *British Medical Journal*, they assume that I know all about their specialty and can understand the jargon and abbreviations that spill from their lips. And though, after they've blinded me with science, they are always generous with medical gossip and suggestions for topics I should write about, they often omit to tell me what I'd like to know about my health. And I, not wishing to upset them, am too polite to ask.

Our joint determination not to play the traditional roles of doctor and patient is well summed up in those remarks of hollow cheeriness with which they try to reassure me—not as a worried sufferer but as a fellow doctor. "Don't worry, it'll be a swift job," said the surgeon who was about to remove my appendix. "I've got tickets to take the family to *My Fair Lady* in two hours' time." He didn't know his patient was a brooding romantic who, when he had earlier been borne from his front door on a stretcher, had gazed on crocuses and spring blossom through the eyes of a man who knew he was looking on the world for the last time.

Early the following morning, a young night nurse prepared with shaking hand to give me some post-operative Omnopon. "I'm terrified," she confessed. "The first time I've given an injection and it has to be a doctor." As she slowly eased the needle through my skin, I suppressed an "Ouch" and congratulated her.

I suspect that's our trouble. When we become patients we

still play the game as if we were at the other side of the net and try to give doctorly reassurance to those who look after us. If an act of treatment is involved, we feel it our duty to allay the anxieties of the person at the other end and both players finish up treating one another.

Our handicap when we try to play the part of patient is our professional need to be polite and reassuring. It's not easy to abandon all those years of conditioning and weep as shamelessly on the pinstriped shoulders of our colleagues as our patients weep on ours.

Games that doctors lose

THE HOLISTIC GAME

ON ONE OF the golden days that occasionally come to Britain at the beginning of November, I drove into the country to have lunch with a one time patient who became a long time friend. A year before he had had what was to him some pretty formidable surgery for the removal of a cancerous growth and, the week we met, was due to visit outpatients to hear what the surgeons wanted to do about something that had cast its shadow on an x-ray film.

But that wasn't what we talked about. We chatted about the things we always do: our work (he too is a writer who was once a scientist), news of our children, gossip about our friends, books we had read, plays and films we hoped to see. I remember little detail of the conversation; what I shall never forget is the mood of contentment that enwrapped my friend. He was clearly at peace with the world and radiated the sort of serenity my memory associates with nuns and monks who live contemplative lives. His mood was infectious and my wife and I quickly succumbed to it. His wife clearly shares it all the time. It was so powerful that I had to comment on it and that was when he told me about his recent medical history.

His treatment, he acknowledged, was a tribute to modern surgery. The right things had been done well and efficiently and he had been shown great kindness and consideration. But after modern technology had done its stuff he found himself cast upon a lonely shore. Modern medicine didn't seem to have any suggestions as to how he could do what he most wanted to do, to "fight" against the disease that seemed set on destroying him.

He searched energetically for the sort of help he wanted and found it only on the medical fringe and beyond. Because he is a scientist, he eventually rejected the rigid mechanics of some of the "fringe" treatments, but he has retained the spiritual qualities that the unorthodox practitioners encouraged him to develop. He is a fortunate man. And I consider myself fortunate to know him because he re-kindled in me a mood that once sustained me through the blacker moments of general practice. He reminded me of the simple but oft-forgotten truth that we all suffer from an incurable disease called mortality which infects us from the moment of conception and is inevitably fatal.

The daily weight of doctors' work can lead them to react to mortality as an enemy to be fought on every front, rather than as an awkward ally which has occasionally to be appeased. I don't suggest we should capitulate in what romantics call our "fight against disease" but I do think that, as our technological weaponry grows more powerful, we need stronger reminders that our purpose is not to wage relentless war against mortality but to seek to improve the quality of the lives of all who suffer from it.

I get irritated when people talk about holistic medicine as if it were a brave new discovery. The best medicine—or what I was brought up to think was the best medicine—has always been holistic, with doctors using their technical skills as wisely and considerately as they can try to restore their patients into some sort of harmony with the world in which we all struggle to survive. I dislike the word "holistic" only because I wish we didn't need a special adjective to describe something that should lie at the heart of every clinical transaction.

My visit to my friend reminded me of another loyalty involved in that transaction. The only worry he expressed was about the visit to the hospital specialist he was due to make that week, because he intended to explain that, though he valued the specialist's advice, he didn't, for reasons of his own, propose to follow it. He was concerned that this rejection might hurt the feelings of a man whom he much admired and asked me how I would couch the message to make it least hurtful. Only later did I recognize the paradox in which he had engaged me: advising a patient on how best to treat his doctor.

Two under-sung achievements of British medicine over the past twenty years have been the development of what is now called the hospice movement and our retention of an effective system of primary care. The hospice movement has not just harnessed the humanitarian urge that most doctors have to help people who are suffering but has encouraged them to use their scientific skills to devise and refine effective ways of treating the symptoms of people who are terminally ill. Every day, doctors who work in hospices practise what others call "holistic" medicine because their purpose all too clearly is not to fight mortality but to assuage it.

Similarly general practice, at its best, is concerned not just with trying to mend minds and bodies but with sustaining the spirit of individuals who are part of a family, part of a community, members of the family to which we all belong. Yet the technical, academic, and administrative demands on GPs seem to grow with every report that is published about their activities and some, like some of their hospital colleagues, no longer have the time to fulfil what is occasionally dismissed as their "pastoral role".

Could it be that we need a special doctor just to guide patients through our complex medical world, to protect their interests, sustain their spirit and, like the hospice doctors, use science and skill to care for all of us who are dying, though the imminence of our deaths is less predictable than it is for the hospice patient?

We used to have such doctors. They were called GPs. Today's bearers of that title are subjected to a form of "vocational training" much praised by those who organize it. Indeed, post-graduate training for doctors is now more complex and more organized than it has ever been, yet increasing numbers of intelligent, rational people like my friend have to search outside orthodox medicine, often fishing in waters that they don't find particularly savoury, in their desperate attempts to find someone to sustain their spirit in the way that doctors once used to do.

THE APPROPRIATE TECHNOLOGY GAME

MOSES SAT ALONGSIDE me on a log outside the Muhimbili Hospital. His appetite for conversation was undiminished by his age—I suspect he was five—nor by the fact that his only English was the phrase "Good evening". He showed us the scar on his chest through which a surgeon had repaired his heart; he listened to the cameraman's Sony Walkman and clicked his fingers to the western music; he even pretended to understand the Swahili spoken by our BBC producer who learned it at night classes in Teddington and who, while fluent, posed problems for anyone unused to Swahili spoken with a Yorkshire accent.

Moses was one of several patients at Muhimbili who had had "high technology" cardiac surgery. Most go to Rome where the operation is free. Some come to St Thomas's in London where the cost—paid by the Tanzanian government—is over £6000, or to other European centres where the cost is similar or even higher. Moses, an enchanting child whose equanimity seemed undisturbed by the fact that his mother had, the day before, returned to her village 200 miles from Dar es Salaam, is alive thanks to "high technology" but let us leave him for a moment, sitting on his log and chatting cheerily to all around him, while we turn to weightier considerations.

A fashionable phrase among those who like to define what they think people in the Third World need—as opposed to what the poor misguided creatures might actually desire—is "appropriate technology". It is a commendable concept and those who play the appropriate technology game before Western middle-class audiences rarely fail to win enthusiastic applause, but when I visited Tanzania in January 1985 a lesson I found it hard to escape was that appropriate technology is useless in the absence of appropriate politics or appropriate economics. An admirable system had been established for bringing appropriate care to the appropriate place—the villages—but was breaking down because many village clinics were deprived not just of medicines but of simple items like wash-basins or even water.

I don't want to diminish what Tanzania achieved under its president, Julius Nyerere, after it achieved independence in 1961. It has been one of the few stable countries in a turbulent continent and Nyerere's brand of socialism, which owes more to the teachings of Christ than those of Marx, produced a genuinely multiracial society—African, Arab, and Asian—united by one language, Swahili, which originally was the language of only the coastal people. But in economic terms it has produced little. The education system is as well organized and as "appropriate" as the medical system but now suffers a desperate shortage of books and other teaching materials. Farmers, compelled to leave their homes and to live in villages, have given up producing the extra food needed by the expanding population because there is no incentive to grow more than they need for themselves. Their co-operatives have been abolished and replaced by state marketing boards that are woefully inefficient. Other state enterprises lurch into catastrophe not because of lack of intelligent top management—of which there is plenty—but because of poor middle management. Tanzania is well endowed with "officers" and "other ranks" but is desperately short of NCOs.

In the cities, shops are almost empty of goods and the currency is debased. The black market value of local money is one fifth that of the official exchange rate and, when Europeans walk along the main street of Dar es Salaam, they raise a susurration of the word "exchange" whispered by locals eager to buy foreign currency. Crime rates in the capital rise as people are driven desperate by hunger. And in the middle of it all sits Moses. When Western enthusiasts play their appropriate technology game, what are we to make of poor inappropriate Moses. He led me to bless those medical ancestors who suggested that our first loyalty as doctors must be to the individual patient who sits in front of us, and that this transcends our responsibility to the society in which we practise. I don't think we should feel guilty if occasional loyalty to an individual leads us to take "inappropriate" action, because it is not only Moses's world that is mad, mad, mad.

The day I returned from Tanzania, two items in one BBC news bulletin told me that our masters had just spent £3 million putting a fence around a missile base but could not raise £270,000 to keep cardiac surgery going at Guy's Hospital in London. Please don't give me the political arguments. I've heard them all before and I know how persuasive they can be, but I want to react now as I reacted when I sat alongside Moses.

In an early novel, *The Anti-death League*, Kingsley Amis puts the following words into the mouth of a character who has indulged in a bizarre irrational act in protest at the nasty things he had seen Nature—or God—do to kind and honest people around him.

"Sometimes you've got to be impractical and illogical and a bit useless because the only alternative is to do nothing at all, and that would be simply offensive. You can't let things go sliding past without any kind of remark as if nobody noticed or cared. It won't do."

Hear, hear, says I. And so, I suspect, say the patients at Guy's. So also, I'm sure, would say Moses—though it might come out sounding like "Good evening".

THE RESENTFUL PRISONER GAME

A JOURNALIST LEARNS early in his career that some topics provoke a dramatic increase in the number of letters to his editor. I mean not a mere doubling or trebling but an inundation, with letters coming not singly but in sacks.

In the late 1960s three topics always produced the sacks: abortion, animal experiments (that one still does), and the Pill. John Rowan Wilson, surgeon and novelist, discovered a fourth. Writing in The Spectator, he suggested the formation of a *Change your job at forty Club*. The letters began to arrive within 48 hours. That very month, I had explored the same theme in *World Medicine*, suggesting that many doctors who were good at their job had extracted most of the personal satisfaction from it by the time they had reached their late thirties, started to get bored, and turned their hands to more dangerous activities like politics or administration. When John rang to tell me about his sacks, I was busy counting mine.

Many of the letters I received made depressing reading. Some came from academics who felt they had now done all the useful research they were likely to achieve and sought my advice on where, outside the mainstream of medicine, they could find work that would challenge their minds and their imaginations. Most came from clinicians whose attitude towards their work had run a similar course: excitement, enthusiasm and involvement in the early days; boredom entering their lives insidiously and, at first, unnoticed as they entered their late thirties. Finally came recognition and acknowledgement of the boredom and a depressing feeling of imprisonment within a career that offered little flexibility and from which the only escape was that distant pension.

A few years later, a consultant physician, Alex Paton, described in the *British Medical Journal* how disenchantment was creeping into his life as a clinician. John Wilson and I wrote to him and discovered that he too had had letters from doctors who were prepared to face up to the truth that medicine, as they were then practising it, seemed unlikely ever again to offer them the challenge and excitement that it had in the early days of their careers and which many of them thought were necessary to make them effective doctors. A lot of doctors seemed to be playing a game they could never win: the resentful prisoner game. Since then medical "career structures" have become even more rigid and I find it hard to escape the feeling that our academic masters, in their commendable desire to raise standards and to tidy things up, have laid too great a stress on neatness and behaved too often as if they were dealing with highly trained organisms and not with un-neat, quirky individuals. In my role of sceptical voyeur, I've even decided that some of the people who make decisions about postgraduate education have taken on the job as *their* escape from a grinding routine that was beginning to get them down. Trips to London or a foreign part, playing committee games, and a little pomp and ceremony make a welcome break from the unending prospect of outpatients, ward rounds, or daily surgeries until retirement. Yet these escapists are the people who, with the best of intentions, impose upon others restrictions that imprison them within the narrowest of careers.

Rigid career structures are also great promoters of mediocrity. I remember some years ago how a young surgical registrar, Peter Steele, took time off from medicine to join the Chris Bonington expedition to Everest. When he returned, he applied for a job at a British hospital and he once showed me the letter he got in reply. In essence it asked why the appointments committee, which had had many applications from people who had assiduously pursued an orthodox career, should waste its time considering someone who had gone off and done something irrelevant like trying to climb Everest. So Peter Steele went to Canada and British medicine, I believe, lost someone who had a lot to contribute to it.

Too many doctors are forced to play the resentful prisoner game. It's time we re-examined the concept that medicine is a lifetime commitment to one speciality rather than to a series of tasks that serve the common purpose of our profession. Some people thrive on a lifetime commitment to one line of work. Others seem to commit themselves only because of anxiety about their professional identity.

It's difficult to abandon habits that give an outward appearance of confidence yet conceal an underlying disenchantment. But isn't it time to make a start? Doctors have already handed over many of medicine's technical manoeuvres to machines. What they should develop are not narrow specialist skills but the creative versatility needed to invent and programme the machines—a quality easily transferred from one sort of job to another. A career in medicine should continually broaden an intelligent person's vision rather than restrict it.

Chekhov, while still practising as a clinician, wrote: "My medical colleagues sigh with envy when they meet me and talk about literature and say how sick and tired they are of medicine. The strange thing is that medicine has had a great influence on my literary work. It has widened the field of my observation and enriched my knowledge."

Postgraduate medical education needs to free the resentful prisoners by promoting enrichment at the expense of disenchantment.

Showing off games

A SORT OF VAGRANCY

MY TRAIN HAD arrived one hour late and I was near to running when I burst into the foyer of the small provincial hotel. The receptionist, I remember, sat behind her desk cleaning the dirt from beneath her fingernails with a long plastic knitting needle.

"Which way to the Balaclava Suite?" I asked.

"You can't go in there," she said. "There's a function on."

I heard my voice proclaim a line of stunning pomposity.

"I am the function."

Whenever I feel a crisis of identity coming on, I remind myself of that moment and reassure myself that I have my own game that gives me a clearly defined role in medicine. That evening, for instance, once I was within the Balaclava Suite, I felt emotionally secure. I knew that, after apologies for absence, minutes of the last meeting, and complicated announcements about the coffee and biscuits, I would hear yet another chairperson announce: "And with us this evening we have Dr Malcolm McDonnell, whom as you all know is not just a member of the General Medical Council but also chairman of *Call my Music*, and, of course, needs no introduction from me."

The I am a Function Game can be fun, or so I keep trying to convince myself as I range around these islands, with or without slides, before or after dinner, with or without Ladies. True I eat more than my share of Aylesbury duckling, Bombe Surprise, and slices of tinned peach with a blob of synthetic cream on the top, but I also meet real doctors who have real jobs and who contrast favourably with the ersatz characters (not unlike that cream on the peach slices) who fancy themselves as public figures and thrust themselves into my daily pathway in search of publicity. (It still amazes me that real doctors should turn up to listen to me, who is just as ersatz as the others, though without the excuse of political ambition.)

Once I'd played the game for a season or two, I realized I was one of a guild whose members, like old-time music-hall performers, trod pathways that crossed and recrossed, usually at railway stations. At Crewe Junction, Peter Bull, on his way to a literary soirée somewhere near Bilston, would ask what the audience was like at the medical society that had booked him for the following month. And whenever I strayed from the medical circuit and turned up at a Ladies' Luncheon, I usually discovered that Lady Barnett had been their last speaker and Kenneth Wolstenholme would be their next. Peter Bull and Isobel Barnett have since moved on to the Great Function in the sky and I miss those secrets that we shared at Crewe. These days, I'm more likely to meet their successors in the Shuttle lounge at Heathrow, Edinburgh, Manchester, Washington, or New York.

The medical lecture circuit is much like that of the luncheon clubs though the hours are more rigorous thanks to doctors being prepared to absorb information in the evening as well as at midday. The late Henry Miller, one time professor of neurology and vice chancellor of the University of Newcastle upon Tyne, defined two kinds of medical lecture: those that contain slides and those that contain original thought. I've found I can manage without either, though slides do have the advantage that they introduce an element of uncertainty. This serves to keep the lecturer awake while the warm darkness that accompanies them encourages the audience to sleep, an arrangement that some would claim approaches the ideal.

Over the years I think I've endured the full repertoire of slide misfortune: slides appearing upside down, sideways, back to front, or being gobbled up by the projector; the projector itself blowing a bulb, blowing a fuse, falling from its perch, once indeed bursting into flames. I even strung together an impromptu narrative to match a set of someone else's slides left in the projector of a Lancashire hotel after the previous evening's meeting of a camera club. I managed the first three without giving the game away but when the fourth turned out to be a mildly indecent exposure of a young woman making an unambiguous gesture with a model of the Blackpool Tower, I took fright and confessed. The medical audience noisily demanded to see the next slide but when they discovered it was only a moody shot of the sun setting over Morecombe Bay, they slipped gently back into the arms of Morpheus.

I must also be near to exhausting the repertoire of chairpeople. Those who get your name wrong are commonplace, as are those who introduce you as last week's speaker or even next's. No less disconcerting are the chairpeople who get everything right, applaud you to your feet, then relax into their seats and fall asleep. The most daunting are those who pass you notes while you are in full flow, such as is she who introduced me at a Ladies' Club in California. I was well into my stride and felt I had my kindly feather-hatted audience almost under my spell when Ms Chairperson passed me a note that read: "Forgive my intruding, but your stable door is unbolted." I was living out every speaker's nightmare, and chuntering away with my flies agape. That moment was only slightly less terrifying than that induced by the Herr Professor in Berlin who rose when I had finished and announced: "You now haf an opportunity to interrogate our speaker."

The saddest of the chairpeople are those who are also the meetings' organizers. Such persons usually greet you at the station or airport and drive you to the appointed place where they park you in a room with a large mug of strong coffee while they keep popping anxiously next door to see if anyone has turned up. Their conversation consists entirely of hints that the audience is likely to be slim. They talk of the atrocious weather, the football on television, the local concert being given that evening by James Galway, John Denver or the Hallé Orchestra, the Annual Ball that most of their members attended the previous night. . . . I long ago concluded that an essential attribute for such a person is indomitable optimism. Beryl Bainbridge has described how a fellow author, invited to address a meeting, found himself, one hour after the meeting was due to start, in a hall that contained only the chairman, the caretaker, and himself.

"Shall we pack it in?" asked the author.

"Not yet," said the chairman. "Best wait for stragglers."

THE HONOURS GAME

NOT FOR THE first time, I wish I'd kept my big mouth shut. Three years ago, when the General Medical Council (GMC) celebrated its 125th anniversary, the president invited me to write an account of the changes I'd seen during my membership and, in my article, I suggested that the banishment of certain symbols from the council chamber had made it look more like a place for work than for religious ceremony.

Among the things I thought we were better off without were the courtroom trappings of the old Disciplinary Committee, particularly the degrading dock in which accused doctors had to cringe while their judge gazed down on them from a magisterial bench. (These days accused doctors sit at a table alongside their legal advisers, symbolically at the same level as their professional colleagues who will examine the propriety of their behaviour.) I also described how a recent president, Lord Richardson, had loosened the procedure at council meetings, quietly banishing the mace, and dropping rituals that gave our proceedings too ceremonial a quality. After those changes, I'd heard members react to speeches with murmurs of dissent and even groans, signs that a debate was taking place and not just an endorsement of decisions taken elsewhere.

When the Registrar wrote to thank me for my article, he said he hadn't known the council owned a mace but he'd instituted a search. And now, to my chagrin, it has returned to our meetings, not tucked away discreetly as it used to be, but prominently displayed on a rack in front of the president where even the most purblind councillor can't miss it. I have no particular aversion to maces. If mayors want to process behind a gilded reproduction of an outdated weapon of war, good luck to them. And the House of Commons mace did allow Michael Heseltine to burn off excess cathecholamines by swinging it around his head when he might otherwise have done something dangerous, like sitting down and thinking.

Yet, if we are to have symbols, I would always vote for appropriate ones. The GMC might hasten its progress along the road to civilization if, instead of using a symbol that harks back to days when men strode around in armour and the size of their club was a measure of their power, it chose one that reminded councillors that they are an arbitrarily selected bunch of fallible doctors stumbling towards consensus views. The president's desk might indeed be more appropriately adorned by a transparent box containing the sort of dust to which all of us, even general medical councillors, will eventually return.

I suspect, however, that one subject on which not even the GMC will achieve consensus is the mace question. Maces, like capital punishment, the Common Market, and Russell Harty, divide the nation into two distinct groups. Anthony Clare, now professor of psychiatry at Bart's, once described how, when the college of psychiatrists was being founded, the longest and most heated discussion was over whether this new, exciting, and different college should have a mace. In the end, he said, the pro-macers won because the anti-macers could not rebut the argument that "a mace will help to open doors".

We shouldn't be too hard on the pro-macers. As we grow older I'm sure we all draw comfort from external symbols of meagre achievement, symbols that may help us to deny the truth of Orwell's observation: "Seen from within, every life is a succession of failures." It would be cruel to deprive a tycoon of

wall-to-wall status in his office furnishings, or a senior ticket-collector of an extra band of gold braid on his cap, and, as a friend of mine pointed out when a mutual acquaintance with little talent and less imagination suddenly became a knight, it did make it easier for his wife to get appointments at the hairdresser.

I do worry, however, when intelligent and kindly persons join the hunt after symbols for their own sake. When I was a young doctor, I and my contemporaries used to recognize a condition in our elders that we called "knight starvation" and were amused by the bizarre antics in which some senior doctors indulged in the chase after ephemeral honour. Those antics assumed a sadder aspect when some of my contemporaries started to indulge in them themselves. I find it painful to recall how one person whom I once admired achieved the honour he so coveted by an act that denied the very qualities for which he'd won respect. But then if someone wants to buy your political support, be it with a free lunch or with a knighthood, you must have something that's worth selling. Often it's your integrity.

Even when honours are deserved, the arbitrary way in which they are bestowed does seem to demean those who have been left out. No one would deny that the doctors who ministered to the injured after the attempted assassination of government ministers in Brighton deserved public recognition. But it would be nice if similar honours flowed regularly to doctors in Northern Ireland who have been showing the same heroic endeavour, day in, day out, for more years than most of us want to remember.

Some of medicine's most irritating creatures are those doctors who brandish the honour they've drawn in the lottery as if it were a hard-won postgraduate degree. Small wonder that many a doctor is angered when she or he sees one colleague honoured while others who are more erudite, have done more for their patients, have made greater contribution to medical science—and are infinitely more agreeable—are not. At least in the days of James I, Pitt the younger, and Maundy Gregory, people knew the grounds on which honour was acquired ... indeed often knew the exact price.

THE IMAGE MAKER'S SUBSTITUTE FOR WISDOM

FOR A TIME I didn't recognize the game that many doctors of my generation were playing, perhaps because capon is out of fashion. I'd come to accept the fair round bellies as part of the scenery but I should have detected the increased incidence of wise saws and modern instances, particularly among those with political or academic ambition.

Some of my contemporaries have been making free with the saws for years. People whom I remember as lively, witty, and intelligent companions have assumed a public persona that is at odds with the character that once served them well. Where once they would have enlivened conversation, they now make observations of paralysing ordinariness and, at the drop of a chairman's gavel, they will rise from their seats to make long boring speeches. Most grieviously of all, they refrain from using their private wit in public places for fear that amusing or penetrating remarks might prove "politically inept". They have, I fear, joined the search for that elusive and overprized quality—gravitas.

Gravitas, the image-maker's substitute for wisdom, has become the Holy Grail of the politically ambitious and the search for it leads people to peculiar behaviour. Just as government ministers tend to wipe the smiles from their faces when confronted by a camera, so doctors with political or academic ambition tend, when drawn into public discussion, to rasp on earnestly and nod wisely at one another as if naught but weighty thoughts were granted admission to their minds.

Offstage many of the gravitas seekers remain as bright as they used to be, though a few of my contemporaries already show signs that the assumed pomposity is beginning to seep into their souls. And pomposity, I fear, is the inevitable fate of those who believe that in order to be seen to be serious, they need to be seen to be solemn.

The sad truth is that the gravitas gamesters are probably acting wisely if they wish to advance themselves. 'Twas said of Adlai Stevenson that he was too lively and intelligent to become President of the United States, just as 'twas said of that wittiest of Englishmen Sydney Smith: "He is a comical fellow but he'll never be a bishop." Like Stevenson, Smith failed to achieve promotion, despite his reply to Bishop Blomfield: "You must. not think me necessarily foolish because I am facetious . . . nor will I comprehend you necessarily wise because you are grave."

I wonder if politicians' undue respect for gravitas accounts for their craft's low standing in public esteem. I'm sure it's gravitas—or, to be accurate, assumed gravitas—that makes politics so boring. We are all party to a conspiracy that ensures that they shan't be fun. As Dr William Somerset Maugham advised us: "Make him laugh and he will think you a trivial fellow, but bore him in the right way and your reputation is assured." I'm not suggesting that we turn medical or academic politics into knockabout farce, simply that we recognize that solemnity is not an essential ingredient of serious discussion nor indeed a sign that serious discussion is taking place.

Life, though serious, isn't always solemn and when someone is prepared to shrug off the trappings of solemnity, the effect can be healthily cathartic. I remember when the General Medical Council, attempting to establish a consensus after the Merrison Report, convened an enormous meeting of representatives of every organization that might be considered to have an interest in medical education. The day was heavy with gravitas and as the meeting crawled exhausted towards its close, the chairman pointed out we had yet to hear from a vice chancellor and had the good sense to call upon the then incumbent at the University of Newcastle upon Tyne. Professor Henry Miller rose laboriously to his feet. "I would just like to say," he said, "that this is the most boring meeting I have ever attended." And there was thunderous applause because he articulated the feelings of many who were present. But then Henry Miller had that sense of an audience that made his lectures not just entertaining but stimulating. The tragedy with teachers like him—and, thank God, there are still a number of them about—is that while many of their ideas, memorable because they arrive dressed in paradox or mischievous imagery, provoke thoughtful persons to re-examine old ideas or generate new ones, they are all too easily dismissed by the gravitas merchants who respond by granting the provocateur a court jester's licence. They smile indulgently at the jokes, miss the serious thought that lies beneath them, then return to life's real business of assuming grave faces and boring one another into oblivion.

I wouldn't, however, suggest that we banish gravitas from medicine. Though dangerous on platforms and in lecture theatres and committee rooms, it clearly has a useful place at the bedside.

A former BMA president, Barry O'Donnell, once told me of an Irish doctor who would always say to the relatives of a sick man: "We'll be a little bit worried about him for the next 24 hours," a remark to which I award full marks for artistic impression. It leaves the relatives with an image of the kindly doctor going about his business the next day with part of his mind constantly concerned about the health of their relative. And whatever the outcome, the wise doctor will appear to have anticipated it. If the patient takes a turn for the worse, the relatives will say to themselves: "He gave us a hint of what might happen but was kind enough to break it gently." And if the patient recovers, as patients have a tendency to do despite the most rigorous of treatment, the doctor's 24 hours of concern is, in some mysterious way, perceived by the relatives to have played a part in the miraculous recovery.

Let us reserve mock gravitas for patients' bedsides, where circumstance compels us to retain some insight into what we are doing, and let us try to reduce its influence on medicine's political and academic life.

That will mean rejecting a long established British tradition. Nearly a century and a half has passed since Sydney Smith said of his brother: "He has risen by his gravity and I have been sunk by my levity."

DID HISTORY REALLY HAPPEN?

THE MEDICAL HISTORY Game doesn't need to be a Showing Off Game but it very often is. I played my first hand in the autumn of 1984, when I was invited to give the William Marsden lecture at the Royal Free Hospital in London. Marsden is said to have founded the dispensary that became the Royal Free after an incident which is a hallowed piece of medical anecdotage recorded in a picture by F. Matania which the Royal Free keeps reverentially on display.

According to the story, Marsden, a young surgeon working in London, was walking home down Holborn Hill late one night in December 1827 when he found a destitute eighteen-year-old girl dying in the porch of St Andrew's Church. He took her by cab first to St Bartholomew's Hospital, then to St Thomas's, and then to Guy's but each hospital refused to admit her even though Marsden assured them she was dying and he was prepared to pay the cost of caring for her and for her burial.

She was refused admission because she didn't have the necessary passport—a letter of introduction from one of the hospital governors. When Marsden pleaded that she be allowed to die in a bed rather than in the street, the Warden of Guy's reminded him that many people died in the streets of London every day. Marsden found the girl a death bed in an attic room in a lodging house and resolved to found a free hospital to which the only passport would be need. Sadly, like many another reforming doctor, he discovered that one of the biggest obstacles to creating such a hospital was the antagonism of the medical establishment of his day.

Thanks to my need to learn more of Marsden and his times, my imagination spent a fair proportion of that autumn in medical London of the nineteenth century—a period that it had visited only rarely. Indeed its last trip had been a brief one prompted by the inaugural Marsden lecturer who one night in his club—and no doubt to aid his research—challenged three distinguished doctors, and me, to recreate the ambience of early nineteenth-century London. It is a measure of the feeling we had for medical history that we could resurrect only the more ribald aspects.

I don't know whether my insensitivity to the reality of history was personal—perhaps related to the way the subject was taught at school—or something shared by a generation which was at school during years when our modern history books were being violently re-written, or whether it is a general affliction of all generations. Certainly, for much of my life, my perception of historical events was as distant and as fantasized as my memory of the schoolrooms in which I first heard of them —as fantasized indeed as F. Matania's picture of the incident in the porch of St Andrew's church in which the dying girl looks as clean and healthy and un-destitute as Joan Crawford playing a down and out in a 1930s film. I had observed, however, that one of the symptoms of established middle-age was a resurgence of interest in matters historical. And now I have reached that comfortable time of life, I too am attracted by history largely, I think, because I have seen enough of the world to accept that though our knowledge may have expanded since William Marsden's day, the attitudes and prejudices that affect the way we apply that knowledge remain much the same.

Time was when if I had read that, 150 years before, dying patients were refused admission to London hospitals unless they had a governor's letter, I would have smiled a superior smile and honoured Marsden for subverting a barbaric system. Such attitudes, I knew, prevailed only in the unreal era called history and we, the enlightened, had left them far behind. Now I am more likely to remind myself that the very week in which I gave the Marsden lecture much publicity was given to an unfortunate woman who was refused admission to a NHS hospital because she didn't have the right credentials. All agreed that she had a several mental illness and that she was in need of care and protection. Her crime was that she didn't suffer from the sort of disease that modern psychiatric hospitals feel they exist to cope with. So instead of being admitted to hospital, she was sent to prison, to join other unfortunates who do not possess a recognized NHS passport.

I also know that every day in modern civilized Britain patients needing hospital care are refused admission because they don't have the right credentials: today's admittable patient needs to have a disease that can be treated, or that the doctors find "interesting", and, above all, must not threaten to "block" a bed.

A London geriatrician defined the need for those credentials when she pointed out that this country has no shortage of beds for geriatric patients. The beds exist, she said, but we insist on filling them with patients with other conditions.

I don't suggest that history supplies easy answers to our problems but it can give us insight into what we are doing. And a necessary first step in any form of progress is an abandonment of self deception. Luckily the insight—and, more important, the energy—that helped William Marsden to succeed, did not die with him. If I were asked to name someone who in our time has proved a worthy successor to Marsden, I would nominate the Sisters of Charity who founded the first modern hospice for the dying—St Joseph's Hospice in London—and whose ideas were energetically espoused by Dame Cicely Saunders. When those nuns and Dame Cicely saw there was a group of patients who didn't have the right credentials for our modern metropolitan hospitals, they created hospitals of their own. And, in doing so, created an international movement which has helped remind most Western countries that we still need hospitals dedicated simply to caring for people, sustaining their spirit, and relieving their pain.

Dame Cicely has also reminded doctors that there are skills to be learned, and knowledge to be acquired about the needs of people who in another part of our minds could be labelled "bed blockers". One of the glories of the hospice movement is that the care it offers is founded not just on kindness and on good intentions but on scientific knowledge and on skill.

That achievement is a more appropriate memorial to Marsden and to the spirit that prompted his action than a dozen cosy anecdotes or a dozen rosy pictures.

Word games

AN ONGOING IN-DEPTH OVERVIEW OF WORD GAMES IN MEDICAL JOURNALS

ONE GAME DOCTORS don't play often enough is Hunt the Cliché. A regular vigorous hunt might suppress a destructive animal that has been allowed to breed too freely in medical journals.

A medical cliché is not just an overworked word or phrase. One currently on the rampage is a stylistic device: the habit doctors have of giving articles and books titles like "The Aging Patient" or "The Doctor and The Patient". Maybe we should call the device "The Distancing Use of the Definite Article" because, to my ear, it sounds like a conscious attempt to avoid the friendlier and more human "Aging Patients" or "Doctors and their Patients". But then Distancing is a game we doctors often play to give the impression of objectivity. The Doctor and The Patient are neat homogeneous entities quite unlike the quirky individuals who clutter up our surgeries and hospitals. The trouble with the definite article ploy is that it gives only an *impression* of objectivity and, when overused, can distance us from useful human observations and blind us to the reality that may lie behind the euphemism.

Another huntable species of cliché is that founded upon an unnecessary noun. These days it's something of a cliché in itself to draw attention to the "situation" situation, but doctors are as susceptible as anybody else to pressure from sports commentators who remain exuberant aficionados, never slow to draw our attention to "a blind-side situation", "a penalty situation" or the fact that we "could be facing an extra-time situation".

Doctors respond to the pressure with observations like "This may reduce the risk of a parenteral feeding situation" but we usually build our clichés on other unnecessary nouns. One of our favourites is "basis" as in "on a professional basis" instead of "professionally", and the ugly "on a continuing (or, even uglier, ongoing) basis" instead of "continuous" or "continually". Another favourite is "period": "over a twelve-day period" instead of "for twelve days". And journal prose would stub readers' eyes less often if we were to stop writing "the majority of" when we mean "most". The simple adjective fits the bill on most (the majority of) occasions.

As tends to happen with clichés, once "the majority of" has sounded the ponderous tone, it continues to echo through the sentence and, when we mean "most people", we feel compelled to write "the majority of the population".

We don't just use nouns to build clichés. Most medical writing contains a surfeit of unnecessary adjectives and adverbs. We're particularly addicted to one small word that can be used as both, yet has had its precision blunted by overuse. "Very" retains its strength in a phrase like "the very ground on which she walks" but we doctors use it as an "intensifier", and use it so often that it loses its power. We've yet to learn that "big" now reads as strongly as "very big".

Weak words grow even weaker when they lean on one another for support, yet doctor writers still bestow that dreariest of accolades, "very important", on anything that impresses them. I suspect doctor readers read through clichés like "very important results" without any kindling of interest. Only if the writers dodge the cliché and use an adjective that reveals why the results impressed them—"unexpected results", "surprising results", "crazy results"—will they rouse a flicker of interest from readers. They may even rouse two flickers if they use no adjective but let the rest of the sentence tell readers why they should be interested. "These (important) results suggest we've all been using the wrong treatment for years." Two other adjectives in serious danger of becoming as impotent as "important" are "significant", which perhaps we should now use only in its statistical sense, and "fundamental" which perhaps we should use only for "pertaining to the fundament".

Some years ago I invited readers of the British Medical

Journal to take a hand at Hunt the Cliché and suggest phrases that medical writers had done to death and were due for peaceful interment, with no flowers please.

The first response came from Bryan Brooke, former professor of surgery at St George's Hospital Medical School in London. He'd composed a sentence which he said started with the new arrivals and moved on to those that were at their peak: "It would be fair to say that we should address ourselves to the ongoing crisis situation in our heritage; at the end of the day, however, it has to be said that we all live in a broad church." He regretted he was unable to include "hopefully" but, in the only position it would fit in the sentence—after "ourselves"— it might recapture for a moment the sense which justifies its use. He also apologized that his sentence was not particularly medical but, 24 hours later, I read three of the phrases he'd pilloried in just one article by a doctor who was playing a low-grade political game. (Another retired surgeon, Horace Fleming of Enniskillen, has invented a commendable game to be played as a diversion during Hunt the Cliché. He pointed out that the best way to debunk a rhetorical cliché is to express the sentiment in different words. Thus "at the end of the day" becomes "at the beginning of the night".) Having dealt with rhetoric, Professor Brooke named two clichés that medical editors have allowed to breed too freely.

The first was "prior to" used instead of "before". (I once read an article that opened with the phrase "Prior to the Reformation", . . . which sounded like an ecclesiastical title created by Henry VIII for the monk in charge of the dissolution of the monasteries.) The second was "elegant" as applied to an experiment. Bryan pointed out that contributors to scientific meetings who wish to congratulate the previous speaker never suggest that the work is clever, or intelligent, or well thought out. It is always elegant. He'd even found a paper in which the author referred to work in her own laboratory as elegant. My *Shorter Oxford Dictionary* suggests that, when "elegant" refers to a scientific process, its meaning is "neat". That's a quality I suppose you might find in a physics laboratory or in a mathematical equation, but it's not a quality I associate with any branch of biology, particularly clinical research which tends to be decidedly un-neat.

Other quarry sighted during the BMJ hunt were misused "anticipates" and warrenfuls of "relationships". Relationship has the pathognomonic sign of a verminous word—it attracts other vermin. In our hunt, it rarely appeared alone but as "ongoing relationship", "conceptual relationship", "methodological relationship", "vocational relationship", "defocused relationship" et cetera, et cetera. Other phrases to be hunted are those that medical writers use out of unthinking habit—"by and large"—and some that are pretentious grasps at Sciencespeak, like "state of the art", or "in depth". My nomination for any Contorted Cliché Award came from a public relations company that invited me to "an in-depth overview"; though the BMJ authors who exhorted us to be "in the forefront of initiating" earn special commendation.

Clichés constipate writers' minds. Writers who rely on them never have to think too deeply about the meaning of the words. And that's why they should hunt them from their work. Doctors who don't write should also hunt them out of concern for the physiology of prose. If we clear threadbare words and phrases from our journals, readers may find it easier to absorb the sense that often lies therein. (That is not a royal "we". If you catch me denouncing sin, include me among the sinners.)

Some might say, though I hope they'd think hard before they did, that "the object of cliché removal is improved communication". I suspect it's time we gave "communication" a rest. Recently, in impish mood, I spent a couple of hours in a medical library trawling through papers that purported to advise doctors on how to "communicate" with their patients or "the general public" (people). My haul of words we could do without included: socialization, issue-oriented, normative, interface, emotional databank (and other computer jargon applied to people rather than to silicon chips), polarization, nondirective, an ongoing collection of ongoings, and three fine specimens of that nonsensical conjunction—the variable parameter.

It was depressing that the best examples I found of words getting in the way of understanding—and, on occasion, disguising the absence of meaning—were in papers on health education, an activity that purports to be concerned with giving people useful information about their health.

If the teachers can't express themselves clearly to one another, what chance have they got with the punters?

And what about the editors? Only a few medical journals, such as the *The New England Journal of Medicine* and the *British Medical Journal* succeed in presenting ideas, information, and opinion in clear, direct, and harmonious prose. Most, I'm depressed to say, offer prose that suggests that the editors consider such a trivial matter as the use of language is no concern of theirs. Consider, for instance, the sensitivity to language shown by the editor who published this: "Recognizing that man is an integral element of an environment which is not only spatially distributed but also temporarily distributed, and that spatial location to be strongly determined by the sequence of events in time, the aim of this paper is to give a state-of-the-art review of health-environment research, with an emphasis on the urban situation."

The title of the article? "Improving our communicative skills".

THE LOHENGRIN GAME

LOHENGRIN, YOU WILL remember, arrives on a swan just in time to save Elsa and promises to marry her as long as she doesn't ask him his name. Yet, hardly has the last bar of the wedding march faded when Elsa, displaying the sort of boneheadedness without which legends would have no plots, asks the forbidden question and Lohengrin catches the next swan back up the Scheldt.

This theme of people losing their power once they are named recurs in fables ancient and modern from *Rumpelstiltskin* through *Turandot* to *Last Tango in Paris*. It is also the source of a doctor's strength in the Lohengrin game.

"Is this throat of mine serious?" asks the patient.

"No," says the doctor. "Just pharyngitis."

"Good," says the patient. The evil has lost its power. It has a name. That's even more reassuring than a treatment and certainly has fewer side-effects.

The Lohengrin game comes in handy in general practice. I played it ruthlessly whenever a patient showed me a prescription or thrust a handful of tablets under my nose and asked: "Is this a drug, doctor?" If I wanted them to take the tablets I said "No"; if I thought they'd be better off without them, I said "Yes".

The late Richard Asher described how doctors use the Lohengrin effect to mislead themselves. In a Lettsomian lecture to the Medical Society of London in 1959 he used Pel Ebstein fever as an example. "Every student and every doctor," he said, "knows that cases of Hodgkin's disease may show a fever that is high for one week and low for the next week, and so on. Does this phenomenon really exist at all? If you collect the charts of 50 patients with Hodgkin's disease and compare them with the charts of 50 cases of disseminated malignant fever, do you really believe you could pick out even one or two cases because of the characteristic fever? I think it is very unlikely indeed.

"Yet if, by the vagaries of chance, one case of Hodgkin's did run such a temperature the news would soon travel round: 'There's a good case of Hodgkin's disease in Galen ward. You ought to have a look. It shows the typical Pel Ebstein fever very well.'"

And I remember as a medical student hearing one of my teachers say: "We must get this chap in. He shows the typical picture and we don't see that very often."

I also remember an uneasy fortnight I spent as a locum in general practice treating the Reverse Lohengrin effect, in which the doctor transfers the labels—and the power—to the patients. In that practice most mothers of children with bellyache seemed to have been told that their child had "acidosis". Most patients over fifty with indeterminate, "funny", or inexplicable minor symptoms seemed to have "low blood pressure"—a condition that occurs rarely and then only in people who have fainted or are severely shocked. After a few days, I discovered both syndromes shared two characteristics; the sufferers were all private patients and their conditions needed regular scientific attention from their GP.

Mothers had to consult him about adjustments needed to their children's diets "to readjust the acidity of the system". Those walking around with "low blood pressure" had to have prophylactic injections of Vitamin B12 to ward off the diverse symptoms their condition seemed to produce. The treatments brought rich rewards, and not just to the doctor. Everyone seemed to benefit. The mothers found a new obsessional purpose in their lives as they strove to balance their children's diets, the children had a ready-made excuse with which to remove themselves from any unpleasing circumstance, and the vitamin injections, because of their pink colour, homed in vigorously on the placebo receptors.

Just how powerful those labels were, I discovered when I broke the first law of locum tenens which is never to change the treatment unless you have compelling evidence that it is actually killing the patient. When I suggested alternative labels or hinted that maybe no label was needed at all, the patients merely withdrew their patronage and accommodated their symptoms until my master's return. I shouldn't have been surprised. A label worn too long becomes part of a person's identity, and none of us want that stripped. Doctors can play the Lohengrin game so powerfully because they have few problems with identity. Many of their patients are less fortunate. Writers, whom you would expect to be accomplished players, often disappoint because they are never quite sure who they are.

Even as sharp minded a writer as Alan Coren, editor of *Punch*, can be out-Lohengrined. A reliable witness has described how one evening when Mr Coren motored too sportingly along a London street, a large policeman waved him down, walked slowly round to the driver's window, and asked: "Now, now, now, what have we here? Some sort of humorist, are we?"

THE ATTRIBUTION GAME

WHEN I FIRST started to write about medicine I had to acquire a new diagnostic skill to help detect the doctors who approached me pretending to offer information while really seeking to use me to pay off old scores on their behalf. At times, when I'm in depressive mood, I feel that far too much grudge-harbouring goes on in medicine, but then I remember that dermatologists probably think there's a lot of skin disease about, and chiropodists a lot of feet. Medical writers just have to accept that they are natural targets for the sort of doctor who gives paranoia a bad name. I still get taken in occasionally and realize too late that the person who engaged my interest had a motive far more venal than the one with which she or he hooked me.

I was an even greater target for the grudge bearers when I was editor of *World Medicine* and, for fifteen years, I carried in my head a list of people whose motives needed closer scrutiny than that normally applied to potential contributors. Yet I never wrote that list down for I believe that editors can grow too sceptical, and we all know that paranoid people do occasionally have something to be frightened of.

I remember, when I was a young GP, taking a psychiatrist on a domiciliary visit to an old lady who complained that the man next door was spying on her. As she told her story, the psychiatrist strolled to the window and found himself under surveillance from her neighbour, who crouched behind a telescope at an upstairs window.

Even more hazardous for editors are the opinions that get attributed to them. When I became editor of *World Medicine*, I decided to turn it into a journal in which any ideas, no matter how unorthodox, could first be promulgated and then, in later issues, set upon by critics. I saw my role as keeper of a forum in which ideas about medicine could be openly discussed and I used to claim that I would publish any idea or opinion, no matter how bizarre it might be, as long as I was convinced it was honestly held and it was expressed in an intelligible way. I also enjoyed publishing articles that were impishly paradoxical, or which hid their purpose behind straight faced irony, in the hope that they might provoke readers to think afresh about some of the daily mundanities we've been conditioned to take for granted.

Most of the issues that generate insecurity in doctors—who have to make real decisions rather than juggle with hypothesis in debate—are not bizarre flights of fancy or off-centre ideas, but dilemmas which will never be solved by consensus agreement as long as doctors hold divergent political, moral, or religious views. On these subjects, too, I published opinionated articles which I suppose the authors thought might change the minds of others but which often seemed mere rallying cries to the faithful, delivered in the same ominous tone as Hagen's rallying cry to the vassals in Act Three of *Götterdämmerung* when he wanted them to witness his destruction of Siegfried. I suspect the vassals left some of my Hagens to deal with Sieg- fried on their own.

It's these everyday contentious issues that get editors labelled and make them suitable quarry for the attribution game. Over the years I suspect I published articles that expressed nearly every shade of moral and ethical opinion about abortion, family planning, euthanasia, genetic engineering, and so on and so on. I also published articles that expressed most shades of political opinion on private medicine, "socialized medicine", the pharmaceutical industry . . . the list of subjects could fill this page but I hope you get the drift.

As it happens I do have personal political and moral views on many of these subjects and, when I wanted to express them, I wrote under my own name. But those were not the views attributed to me.

There is a subdivision of Sod's Law designed for editors; just as there is a form of blindness that afflicts the deeply committed. Whenever I published opinions from opposite sides of vigorously contested argument, each side presumed I let their opponents have their say because I was biased in the opponents' favour. Those argumentative folk who play the attribution game, rarely, it seems, read articles with which they agree—more likely they glance at them but find them too boring to remember —but they devote assiduous attention to any argument that angers them, as if they need a regular fix of self-righteousness to sustain their beliefs.

The result, enunciated in the form of O'Donnell's Third Law of Human Perversity (Laws One and Two will have to stay under wraps until another day) is that if an editor publishes two strongly held opinions on a contentious issue, each side will decide that the editor's personal views coincide with those of the opposition. As an editor, I had a bizarre collection of beliefs heaped upon me by attribution gamesters. In the eyes of some readers, I was pro-abortion; in the eyes of others, my religious beliefs blinded my attitude to abortion law reform. (I still have a letter that accuses me of being "a killer of unwanted babies", which I keep pinned to another that arrived on the same day and in the same post accusing me of being "responsible for the misery suffered by unwanted children".) In the eyes of other, equally passionate people, I was a lackey of the wicked drug industry, an enemy of private enterprise, a fascist, a communist . . . you name it and, at some time I was angrily accused of being it. I suspect I am one of the few people to have been sued by an organization of which I was a member.

I used to console myself with the thought that if the flak kept coming from every direction, I was probably doing a reasonable job. The only person who subverted that complacent attitude was the late Sir Denis Hill, a man for whom I had enormous respect. He once told me, in characteristically kindly but forthright style, that it was immoral for me as an editor to publish views with which I profoundly disagreed. I argued with him but I never convinced him. I hope I convinced myself.

The problem presents itself not just to editors but to clinicians. How far should a doctor go in imposing on his patients decisions that have their origin in the doctor's own moral and religious views? There's a good subject on which to publish strongly held opinions. I suspect I've already been labelled by the attribution gamesters on both sides for even mentioning it.

Household games

HE WHO PLAYS THE FATHER

EACH SUMMER, THE long school holidays usher in intensive
weeks of practical parentcraft. It's chilling for to reflect that
those picnics and boat trips and all that bucket and spadework
on the beaches may one day be endowed with mystical properties in our children's memories. Doris Lessing has described
how we use our parents as recurring dreams, "to be entered
into when needed; they are always there for love and hate."

She was writing in *Fathers: Reflections by Daughters* (Virago), in which twelve women describe the bond – usually,
though not always, of loyalty and love – that linked them to
their fathers. I'm happy to commend the book if only because,
when I was a family doctor, fathers seemed to loom larger in
my patients' lives that they did in my textbooks. Indeed, in the
first large textbook on infant development and care published
this century, the word "husband" appeared only once . . . and
that in the sentence: "During this illness, the mother will need
to husband the strength of the child."

Ms Lessing's words disturbed me because I've always had a
deep affection for my father and, though he died in 1957, I still
feel so close to him that I do occasionally wonder whether I
invented him. Have I perhaps turned him into the mystical
Our Father who emerged on so many pages of the Virago book?

"We have at least two fathers," says a note on the cover, "the
real material one who changes, like us, as he get older; and the
other, interior, mythical, father, who is present inside us and
does not change."

Yet those "material" fathers can influence our lives every bit as much as the mystical ones. Even in societies where women's roles are changing, the father is still the family's chief bearer of tidings and experience of the rougher corners of the world outside. And it's difficult to separate his personal talents, the job he does (and the lessons he has learned from it) from his emotional role.

The abiding memory I have of my father is of conversations we had about medicine as we walked through the cemetery opposite our house. He was a GP in a Yorkshire colliery village and used to say that all doctors' houses should overlook cemeteries to remind them of their ultimate failure. When I was a medical student, he would suddenly say "Let's take a stroll amid my mistakes" and, while we walked, he would pass on

ideas about medicine that have proved more enduringly practical than much I learned in medical school. Indeed a lot of what I have written about medicine over the past twenty years derives from those conversations. He would punctuate his tutorial by pausing in front of gravestones, sometimes to explain how the bones beneath might have lingered a little longer above the earth if he had been a little wiser, sometimes to illustrate the social history of the village . . .

Mary T., aged 17, who died of septicaemia after an illegal abortion, lying alongside her father who suffocated underground in the big fire at Yorkshire Main the day before his daughter planned to tell him she was pregnant . . .

Ernie C. the colliery clerk who worked in the office and wore a stiff collar from Monday to Friday but on Saturday nights donned a black cloak and hood to wrestle in working men's clubs as The Rotherham Phantom . . .

Big Stan H. who, at the age of 64, married a girl of 17 and died on his honeymoon in Blackpool of what his young widow told my father was "pneumonia brought on by bronchial ecstasy" . . .

Sometimes we paused on our walks just to adduce further evidence for my father's Law of Headstones: "The more unctuous the inscription, the more unscrupulous the rogue who lies beneath." And occasionally we would stop and gossip with the cemetery keeper, Tom Lyons, an ex-miner who'd been given the job by the parish council because of his skill not as a grave digger but as a gardener. Each summer he would garnish his sombre preserve with beds of flowers that spelt out uplifting messages like God is Love, though one memorable year his spring message was Doncaster Rovers for the Cup.

Tom grew the flowers in a greenhouse tucked away in a corner of the cemetery and there also he grew pound upon pound of fine tomatoes which he would hand to my father and myself in brown paper bags.

"The finest tomatoes in Yorkshire," my father would say to my mother. "Can it be that Tom has access to a mulch denied to the rest of us?" And my mother would twitter "Don't be disgusting, Jim" and tell me to be sure to wash every one under the tap before I ate them.

I have other memories of my father, of course. Of the

embarrassment he caused me by singing too loud in church, and by resting his bottom on the bench when he was kneeling. (I knew, because I'd been told it at school, that well-brought-up people knelt up straight.)

And I also remember his funeral. How a huge crowd stopped us on the outskirts of the village and how a party of miners took the coffin from the hearse and carried it on their shoulders through the streets to the church. I remember the thronged churchyard noisy with gossip until the coffin arrived and then the silence that lasted until Mrs Tierney struck up a hymn on the harmonium and everyone in the yard and street joined those in the church in singing with the sort of vigour in which most of them indulged only when a West Riding team got to Wembley.

I remember trying to analyse what a man had to do to earn such love. Certainly not big things; they were celebrated with honours and decorations and commemorated by Abbey choirs. A bare-headed crowd on a February morning, a loyal hymn, and an honest declaration of love were earned by smaller things: a monotonous accumulation of small acts of sympathy and kindness, and occasional understanding, that the bestower rarely remembered because they were rarely offered consciously. That was the last lesson I learned from father.

The scene moves on. I have a teenage son whom I'm happy to mention only because I know he's unlikely to read these words for many a year. And suddenly I find myself not just ill-equipped but incapable of playing the role in his life that my father played in mine.

Does the fact that I can't even aspire to the role, reveal that my memory of that kind, jovial, somewhat eccentric, character whom I thought was my father really *is* a creation of my dreams? And if I have "fictionalized" my father, how do I stand with Freud? Where was Oedipus while we walked through the cemetery? Where was the jealous hatred that a son is alleged to harbour for his father because of the unacknowledged desire he has for his mother? The answer seems to be that Freud got it wrong. Neil Kessel, professor of psychiatry at the University of Manchester, has suggested that it is Oedipus's dad who sees the child as the rival for the mother's affection, rather than the other way round. The child, he points out, knows only the state into which it is born but the father experienced sole rights to the affection of the woman before his rival appeared. Even in the legend it is Laius, the dad, who first tries to kill Oedipus, the son.

Neil Kessel's hypothesis would explain why children of both sexes can suffer Oedipal conflicts. The most persuasive argument he deploys is that, in a long clinical career, he has never seen a patient in which conflict could not be accounted for in terms of his hypothesis rather than that of Freud.

THE RETIREMENT GAME

MY NAME AND address have fallen into the hands of a clutch of finance and insurance companies that cater for GPs retiring from the NHS. Nearly every post now brings a mailing that invites me to Book Now for my Indian Summer.

On my last birthday, the first envelope I opened turned out to be an advertisement disguised as a birthday card. "Look forward," it said, "to those well-earned days of retirement. Judicious investment now will ensure that their happiness remains unmarred by financial insecurity."

It's not the sort of thing a man wants to read on his birthday, particularly a man who is notoriously young for his age. Surely it was only yesterday I suffered those stumbling aspirations of immaturity when I had to keep reminding myself there were other things in life besides sex though, at the time, I could never remember what they were. Come to think of it, it was only yesterday. Thursday.

A lot of my contemporaries who are still GPs seem to have grown unhealthily concerned with the rules of the retirement game. And, as an addicted reader of local newspapers, I've noticed that GPs, or more precisely, those GPs who've managed to survive their working lives, seem to relish the actual rubric of retirement. Usually there's a gathering in a local hall when the old boy's patients, feeling guilty perhaps over the havoc they've wreaked in his coronary arteries, come together to eat cupcakes and give him a gold watch and a cheque to carry across the threshold to oblivion.

The GP's speech of thanks, at least according to local re-porters, follows a traditional pattern: an expression of humble thanks, an explanation of the joy derived from every second of a hard working life, and an admonition to young fellows coming into the profession today who don't seem to have the same qualities of self-sacrifice and dedication that we had in our time. I always assumed that final sentiment is a two-fingered gesture of farewell to all others who at that moment have their heads down in their surgeries. Indeed, I imagine the old boy reeling off the words in a monotone while his attention is focussed on slipping his finger discreetly into the fold of the cheque he's just received to catch a glimpse of the number of digits that nestle alongside the £ sign.

My father who was a GP took a more positive attitude to retirement. He saw it as a time to extract some retrospective pleasure from the hard slogging that preceded it. He intended to go on living in the house from which he'd practised so that whenever the door bell rang he could answer it wearing old clothes and affecting a gross tremor.

"Oh, I'd love to help you," he'd tell the patient on the doorstep, "but, as you can see, the old health has let me down. Still, a clever new doctor has moved in down the road. Let me give you a tip—a secret I can pass on now I'm no longer in the business. This new fellow's brain functions much better at night. So don't call him now. Wait till he's had an hour or two in bed. Then you'll get him at his best."

I hope my father got a lot of pleasure from contemplating that scene because he never made it. One cold winter's night, like many a GP who is cynical in word rather than in deed, he insisted on doing his evening surgery with a crippling pain in his chest and, as it turned out, a large infarct in his heart. I still feel guilty that, after his death, we didn't fulfil a wish he'd expressed one evening, years before, after he'd had a good dinner with a couple of GP friends. Egged on by them, he'd described the headstone he would like to see erected over his grave. It was to be a simple slab of Connemara marble with an electric bell embedded in its centre. And beneath the bell-push would be the carved inscription: "You can ring like hell but you can't get me now. Yours in peace, James Michael O'Donnell."

Maybe my memory of my father's exit influenced my own

premature retirement from general practice in 1964. I'd enjoyed family doctoring but, after twelve years of it, I was growing weary. If I'd stuck it out for a bit longer, I'd have experienced the resuscitation of general practice engineered by Kenneth Robinson, the Minister of Health who introduced the Doctor's Charter. And I suspect that would have encouraged me to stay on. But I was young and impatient. I just knew that general practice in 1964 was at a low ebb, indeed had ebbed so low that I felt high and dry, and I decided to escape. It's not the sort of decision that a chap makes every day of his life and I felt its announcement needed a bit of a hype. At the end of an evening surgery, I crept into the sitting-room and slipped Siegfried's funeral march on to the record player. Then I summoned my wife with a loud, yet gentlemanly, command.

The result was bathos. She was washing her hair at the time and we got involved in a shouted exchange up and down the stairs, with her saying it would have to wait and me implying she was missing an appointment with destiny. Eventually we woke our nine-month-old baby and I had to put in fifteen minutes of cradling and cooing before my wife was prepared to listen to me, her face glowering beneath a cone of Turkish towelling.

"I'm giving it up," I said.

"About time," she said. "You know we can't afford it and it's beginning to make you fat."

"Not that. I'm giving up my job, general practice, medicine, the whole bloody caper."

Her eyes flickered towards the bedroom where our children lay asleep. Then she gazed at me carefully for a full minute. And then, miraculously, she smiled.

"Good," she said and, after kissing me on the cheek, went off to dry her hair.

Next day I wrote to my local Executive Council (fore-runner of today's Family Practitioner Committee) giving six months' notice of my departure, though, under my contract, I needed to give only three. I then composed a valedictory notice for my waiting-room to tell my patients not only when I was going, but why. I tried to keep it crisp and clear but it ended as an ill-blended mixture of the styles of the American Declaration of Independence, Sidney Carton's speech before the guillotine, and a warning notice about venereal disease.

Three months later I began to wonder when the Executive Council was going to circularize my patients to tell them of their impending loss. I rang the man who signed those rude letters I got whenever I "threw unfair pressure on the clerical staff" by returning patients' notes too slowly or sending too many at once.

"Not to worry doctor," said a lugubrious voice at the other end of the phone. "Informing the patients is our responsibility and, as you know, the patients' welfare is our primary concern."

When nothing had happened by D-Day minus eight weeks, I rang again. "Funny you should ring today doctor," said Lugubrious. "The file is on my desk at this very minute. We've got the business of circularizing the patients in hand but there is one other little matter, so unimportant that I apologize for troubling you with it.

"I've a form here that we have to return to the Ministry and I see we have no entry under the item 'Reasons for resignation'. Shall I put it down as leaving the district, returning to hospital work, ill health, or miscellaneous?"

"Just write 'Despair'," I said.

"Ha, ha, doctor. A most felicitous quip. But what shall I put on the form?"

"Despair," I repeated. "You'll find it in the dictionary under D. And don't forget to tell my patients I'm going."

Three weeks later I got a phone call from an even more lugubrious person, one rung further up the Executive Council ladder. "Won't take a minute of your time, doctor, just a little matter of a form. Not really important but we don't seem to have your reason . . ."

"Despair," I said.

"This pair of what, doctor?"

I spelled out the word for him.

"And by the way," I added, "when are you going to write to my patients?"

"Rest assured Doctor, we have the matter in hand."

From then on I got weekly phone calls from humourless characters residing at strategic points along the paper trail from Executive Council to Ministry of Health. All wished to raise "an unimportant little matter", all assured me they were on the very point of writing to my patients, and all left an indelible impression that defacing their official form with an emotional word was something that Mummy would think very naughty.

The Surrey Executive Council did eventually circularize my patients to say I was going—six months after I'd left. By then, even though, in a primitive bid for survival, we'd changed our telephone number, my wife had clocked up weeks of unpaid service to the NHS answering the door and redirecting the anxious souls she found hovering outside.

We learned about the circular letters when a small girl brought one to the house. It was addressed to her grandfather and, as it mentioned my name, her mother thought I should see it. Unfortunately, her grandfather hadn't been able to read it. He'd died four weeks before it arrived.

THREE PRIVATE GAMES

I'VE NOW LIVED in the same place for 27 years. It's really a suburban dormitory town that abuts on London's Green Belt but some of us old hands still call it "the village" out of habit.

If we wanted a title that caught the spirit of the contribution made to our environment by local builders and planners, we'd probably settle for "urban conurbation". Yet though I've lived among the same people for 27 years, I have lived in three quite distinct communities, and the distinction has lain not in my surroundings but in me. Only now do I realize that I have played three different games without appreciating I was playing even one.

For the first seven years, I was a local GP and had privileged access to the lives of many of the people. It really is an enormous privilege—far greater than that granted to lawyers or others who think they have access to confidences—to be allowed to observe how people behave behind the social façades, to know the mundane anxieties and insecurities that plague the lives of persons of seemingly brazen confidence, to be aware of secret unacknowledged acts of courage. . . . Anyone who has spent more than a month in general practice will know what I mean.

In those days I was also aware of the diurnal patterns of the community. Sometimes, as I drove around visiting patients, I would, at different times, see the same woman drive her husband to the station, drive her children to school, load her car outside the grocer's, park outside the dentist's. I knew who played bridge with whom, and often on which days, who would visit the sick and do their shopping, who was a helpful neighbour and who would make a great show of being helpful while being more a hindrance. Again, any GP will recognize the sort of folk knowledge that came my way.

Then one day I hung up my stethoscope and, for eighteen years, worked in a series of offices in London. The community became a base from which I commuted. I knew nothing of what happened there on weekdays: I was part of it only in the morning, in the evening, and at weekends, which I tended to spend immured within my Englishman's castle. The people I met at the station, on the train, in the High Street on a Saturday morning, at an occasional party (once you cease being a GP, you lose the most believable excuses for not attending), I had to accept on the terms on which they offered themselves. I was no longer privy to the fears, the anger, and the jealousies that underlay the social game. The community became a more arid place than that I had known as a GP. With a shameful lack of

insight, I blamed the change on developers who were unprepared to let one Victorian house stand where twenty "Neo-
Georgian Town Houses" could be crammed in. I put up with
the place because of its convenience and because my children
were happy at the local schools.

Five years ago I started to work at home again; not as a GP
this time but as a writer. Now elements of the two communities
I knew before have come together. The place *has* been overbuilt
and overcrowded but it does contain real people and not just
commuting troglodytes. Once again I'm aware of the diurnal
pattern when I walk across the cricket green on my way to the
post office to despatch an article or script to some foreign part,
or when I ride my bike down to W. H. Smith's in the High
Street to buy some paper-clips or rubber bands. I may not be
privy to people's secrets but I recognize individuals, know the
time they are likely to be coming out of the library, know who's
likely to be playing bowls on a Tuesday afternoon, know which
mothers are likely to have taken their children to the swings
at the "rec" in mid-morning, which in mid-afternoon. I've also
become aware of things the community does as a community,
the "bring and buys", the "continuing education" classes, the
enthusiasm for first aid, for archeology, for "keep fit", indeed
for a bewildering range of activities that bring people together.
Some communities, such as mining villages, derive their identities from a common occupation; ours exists through its determination to get local people to fight off loneliness by doing things
together.

A few weeks ago, an ex-patient of mine got me to give a talk,
"with slides", to the local branch of a national charity. It was
a sunny summer's evening and, as I walked to the appointed
place, across the park and recreation grounds, I passed the
familiar sights: the noisy children on the swings and slides,
the solemn warfare on the bowling green, the notices outside
Churchfields Hall advertising courses in conversational French
and outings to National Trust gardens. My main memory of
the meeting itself is of wonder at the work that had gone into
organizing it, selling tickets, preparing the food, soliciting
prizes for the raffle, and the hundred other tasks that ensured
the evening was not just fun but raised a useful sum of money.
The chairman won polite applause when he gave account of

how much money had been raised by previous meetings and, for a couple of hours, I felt as much part of the community as I had been as a GP.

When writing of such an evening, it's easy to sound patronizing; I hope I've avoided that. Just as it's easy to denounce the need for charity and demand that all socially useful activities be supported directly by the state. Yet I can't help feeling that in communities like ours the actual means of raising money does as much for the community as the money does for the charity. We must not, however, take it for granted. The money that was raised that evening will be used to finance medical research, as will the £6,000 raised the previous weekend by a local actor who got his friends to play in a "celebrity" competition at a local golf club. The people who organize the sort of meeting I attended, and actors who give up the only day of leisure in their week, do so because they think medical research is worth supporting.

I trust that those who actually use the money—and who may well be "commuter members" of the communities from which they travel to their laboratories—remind themselves occasionally of the thousands of small acts of good will that, when added together, provide them with their resources.

Political games

THE BOOZE GAME

I HAVE A chum who gives up alcohol each Lent not so much to mortify the flesh as to exorcize a fear. It's a fear that, I suspect, haunts many of us who have a drink on most days of our lives. If we catch ourselves looking forward to that drink, we start to wonder how close we are to being dependent on it.

I've never fancied being a teetotaller and that may be one reason why, in 1985, BBC Television invited me to examine the drinking habits of my fellow citizens. The series was called *O'Donnell Investigates . . . Booze,* a title that suggested to my friends that I was merely revealing the results of a lifetime of research. What I saw when we made the programmes didn't put me off the stuff but it gave me a nasty shock. Not for the first time I found that my attitudes were based on experience which, while I was looking in another direction, time had quietly subverted. And I soon discovered that doctors who are called on to cope with the effects of alcohol on their patients are drawn, whether they like it or not, into a political game.

Over the past twenty years the incidence of alcohol abuse has doubled. And our government which, in 1985, launched a panic campaign because the number of "drug addicts" had reached 50,000, turns its back on another million addicts who can be labelled "alcoholics". Not our problem, said the then junior health minister, John Patten, though a wealth of evidence showed that it was.

We grow impervious to the statistics. Some three million people in Britain suffer the catastrophic medical and social effects of alcohol abuse. In 1983 the cost—losses to industry,

demands on health services and police, damage to property, and so on—was at least £1,600 million. In 1982 there were 98,000 convictions for drink and driving. These are just numbers that a newsreader reels off in the background while we're busy ordering another round.

No one wants to be a killjoy. And plenty of people are eager to advise us not to worry. Have another drink and cheer yourself up. Your drinking habits are protected by a lobby that no politician wants to upset. The government is more dependent on alcohol than any alcoholic, thanks to £4,000 million a year in taxes. Small wonder that, in the late 1970s, when the government Think Tank produced a report recommending action to curb alcohol abuse, both Labour and Conservative governments not only ignored it but seemed to want to bury it. We know its contents only because it was later published in Sweden.

A couple of nights I spent in a hospital casualty department while we were making the programmes, taught me not to equate alcohol abuse with "alcoholism". It has more blatant manifestations, like domestic violence and football hooliganism. A fracas that erupted in 1985, when Millwall "fans" visited Luton, was such an outrage that even newspapers that traditionally show a deep concern for the well-being of big-spending advertisers mentioned that the young people who ran amok were drunk. At the time, MPs and leader writers were quick to prescribe treatment. Therapists on the left saw the rioters as victims of the government's social and economic policies; those on the right saw them as candidates for birching or for "short sharp shocks". None suggested that the chancellor, Nigel Lawson, who was adding a final polish to his budget at the time, might ease the problem by dramatically raising the price of drink. Yet the evidence is overwhelming that alcohol abuse is directly linked to the real price of drink, its price related to earnings.

In Britain that price has been steadily declining. In 1938 a manual worker had to work eighty and a half hours to earn a bottle of whisky. In 1960 he earned it in six hours, and by 1976 the time had dropped to two and a half hours. In 1938 it took him 24 minutes to earn a pint of beer. In 1960, it took him twelve minutes, in 1976 nine. And as the price has declined, the number of "outlets" has increased—in many streets, off-licences, wine bars, and licensed restaurants heavily outnumber pubs—and consumption has risen, particularly consumption by teenagers and young adults.

Until I looked at the figures, and at the victims, I wasn't overconcerned about youthful drunkenness. Young people have always enjoyed drinking too much, and few of my contemporaries would claim that our generation of medical students was abstemious. But our drunkenness was on a different scale. In the late 1940s we could afford to get drunk on two, maybe three, nights a week. Now many young people can afford to get drunk nearly every night.

Having examined the evidence in sceptical—and defensive —mood, I am persuaded that alcohol abuse is directly related to the general level of alcohol consumption, and that consumption is related to availability and to the real cost of drink. The liquor trade argues that increasing the cost of drink puts an unfair burden on the innocent social drinker without altering the behaviour of heavy drinkers. That argument is rebutted by a mass of evidence. Research in Lothian, for instance, showed that a modest price rise produced a fall in harmful effects among heavy drinkers. I conclude regretfully that the price of reducing alcohol abuse, and its horrifying social and medical effects, is one we all will have to pay, or at least all of us who enjoy drinking.

Our grandparents knew this when they built solid Temperance Halls dedicated to the defeat of the demon drink. At the turn of the century, the cause of temperance generated a great mass movement involving not just individuals but families. In 1901 there were, for instance, 29,000 junior Bands of Hope— one for every four pubs—and three and a half million children were members. In those days the Salvation Army and other temperance organizations were vocal and dedicated because, in crowded city slums, the effects of drunkenness were all too visible. They campaigned vigorously for restrictions on the supply of alcohol because that seemed the obvious way to reduce drunkenness. The liquor trade labelled them as killjoys but, with the coming of the First World War, they won some unlikely allies. In 1915 the Shipbuilding Employers' Federation asked the government to restrict the sale of drink because it was causing a grave loss of production. Lloyd George endorsed their request: "We are fighting Germany, Austria, and the drink. And, as far as I can see, the greatest of these deadly foes is drink." The generals also backed restriction. Lord Kitchener adjured the nation not to treat soldiers to drinks so that they could "do their duty to their country in a thoroughly efficient manner". (Could it have been that young men "died better" when they were sober?) And King George V gave the King's Pledge that drink would not be served in the Royal Household until the war was over.

In 1915 Britain got its licensing laws which were based on the belief that alcohol abuse could be reduced by restricting the supply of alcohol. And they worked. Their effect on abuse showed up in medical statistics which revealed, for instance, a sharp decline in deaths from cirrhosis of the liver.

Then, in 1919, the United States went one stage further and introduced Prohibition. The side-effects of Prohibition, particularly the glamorization of law-breaking, discouraged legislators in other countries from following the US example. They sought an alternative and my profession obliged by supplying a disease called alcoholism.

Public policy could now be based on the proposition that alcohol itself was not dangerous and caused trouble only when abused by a minority of people who had an innate inability to handle it. The flaw lay not in the drink but in the drinker. Countries that wanted to avoid Prohibition eagerly embraced this proposition and doctors tried to understand and treat "alcoholics". I remember being taught in the 1950s that the liver disease and vitamin deficiencies suffered by alcoholics were not so much effects of a toxic drug as the result of malnutrition. Alcoholics, we were told, ate inadequate diets and the effect of high alcohol concentrations on the lining of their gut prevented proper absorption of vitamins.

That dogma sounded less convincing when researchers showed that, even in people on enriched diets, heavy drinking could produce alcoholic liver disease. And in 1962, a British psychiatrist, Dr D. L. Davies, subverted another tenet of the prevailing dogma when he described how seven previously alcoholic patients had become normal social drinkers.

Maybe the flaw didn't lie in the individual after all.

Davies's work seemed to change the emphasis in alcohol research which has since accrued impressive evidence that alcohol abuse is indeed linked to the general availability of alcohol and to its consumption not by a genetically programmed or "sick" minority but by us all. In every country that has been studied, increases in per capita consumption have been paralleled by increases in all the indices of alcohol damage. So the Salvation Army, the Band of Hope, and the other temperance campaigners were right when they made the seemingly obvious assumption that alcohol abuse was related to alcohol consumption, and that consumption depended on supply.

We have come full circle, but with one big difference. Eighty years ago, powerful religious and social forces kept people and government aware of alcohol abuse. Today most people don't know how great the problem is. Many suffer the effects behind closed doors, and when drunkenness erupts in the streets we call it something else, like hooliganism.

I don't advocate prohibition. I merely suggest that a country where drink is available must accept some level of alcohol abuse and we need to discuss how high that level should be. Most dispassionate observers consider the level in Britain is now too high.

The Think Tank report that got buried concluded that only government could make a significant impact on the level of abuse, and recommended that consumption be curbed by preventing drink from getting cheaper. Yet, in November 1984, John Patten told a BMA conference that our present government had no intention of taking any action to curb alcohol abuse. It was not a government responsibility, he said. It was up to the doctors to deal with "alcoholism".

Maybe he never saw the evidence that found its way to Sweden.

THE NATIONAL ILLNESS GAME

THIS GAME CAN be played in newspapers or on radio but is most often played on television.

"It's high time, Sir Robin, that this country faced up to reality . . ."

The player—usually an MP, a concerned doctor, or a caring spokesperson—pauses for a moment to allow the audience to shade its eyes against the brilliance of the insight that is to follow.

". . . and the reality is that what we have at the moment is not a National Health Service but a National Illness Service."

The speaker smiles triumphantly and the audience, stunned by the originality of the observation, is at first silent then bursts into enthusiastic applause. The scene merits a five star entry in any compendium of Great Medical Clichés of Our Time. Yet, like most clichés, the phrase "National Illness Service" still gets unquestioning acceptance. It's time surely to re-examine some of the assumptions it takes so easily for granted.

What's so wrong with a National Illness Service? Could it not be a more socially useful institution than some of the crazier

edifices that have been erected in the name of health? Does
health really lie within the gift of doctors or is its presence or
absence controlled by politicians? What on earth is health,
anyway?

To assault the last question first, I find Health almost imposs-
ible to define. The World Health Organization draws on fantasy
for its definition: "a state of complete physical, mental, and
social well-being." On the day humans achieve that state, they
will also be able to lie back and watch the pigs wheel lazily
overhead. Health, I suspect, is more closely related to happiness
than it is, say, to physical wholeness.

Many of my patients who suffered from chronic and often
severely debilitating diseases seemed to live "healthier", and
certainly happier, lives than those who *knew* they were physically fit, because they had the x-rays and the expensive annual
physical "check-ups" to prove it, though they lived in acrimoni-
ous disharmony with their environment. Notions of health are
clearly individual. The track-suited persons who jog past my
house obviously interpret health in terms of physical fitness.
And good luck to them even though I think their interpretation
is based on a fallacy—the fallacy enshrined in the words of the
jogger who gazed down sadly at the friend who had just dropped
dead while jogging alongside him: "What a way to go. In the
peak of condition."

My notion of health means it lies more within the gift of
politicians than of doctors because it depends more on the
provision of sanitation and housing and on political measures
like the Clean Air Act than on the relief of anxiety and pain.
Not that I wish to diminish the importance of relieving suffering; that's why I think an illness service is every bit as commendable as a health service. While politicians deal with the
health of communities, doctors and nurses generally concern
themselves with the illness of individuals. I don't deny that
some doctors have been, and still are, first-rate public health
administrators, imaginative and energetic. I merely suggest
that, although doctors can act as advisers and campaigners,
health depends in the end on political action. John Snow
mapped the pattern of cholera in the Soho epidemic and doctors
then argued for 30 years whether cholera was a waterborne
disease. Meanwhile the politicians got rid of cholera by

encouraging Sir Joseph Bazalgette and his fellow engineers to build London's sewers.

In less distant times, the postwar housing drive and the Clean Air Act probably had a greater effect on people's health than medical "breakthroughs". And, more recently, politicians have voted in favour of health in the form of compulsory seat-belt wearing in cars and will need to do so again if we are to cut the mortality caused by cigarettes and move our national diet in a healthier direction. Doctors can weigh in with advice and with campaigning vigour but the health giving action will have to come from politicians.

Meanwhile, why don't we wipe the tarnish from the notion of a "National Illness Service". Caring for sick and disadvantaged individuals has always been the doctor's main contribution to society. Modern medicine has come unstuck only when it has lost contact with that tradition. Scientific knowledge and tech-nical skills can become ends in themselves but they remain important to clinicians because they allow them to relieve suffering. High technology is not an enemy but an ally when clinicians use it to heal rather than to show off. I am impressed, for instance, by the way transplant surgeons in this country— as opposed to some transplant surgeons in some other countries —when they are called on to make public pronouncements, usually argue fiercely on behalf of their patients rather than on behalf of their speciality or of themselves.

Sadly, it is only when people are ill that they fully appreciate the virtues of the illness service that our profession provides. Certainly when I'm a patient I'm happy to let others pursue the fantasies of the WHO definition while I settle for a more mundane "patch up" job from kindly doctors who can remove my gangrenous appendix, zap the pathogens that invade my bronchi, and who one day may have to replace my worn-out hip joints. They may not be advancing the concept of Health, as it is seen by deep thinking gamesplayers at weekend seminars in country houses, but in these islands the patching up is done by skilled persons, most of whom still evince concern about our plight as individuals.

Until we've actually built the New Jerusalem, I suggest we should be grateful for the skill and understanding we can meanwhile find at the dear old Slagthorpe Memorial. To play a game that uses National Illness Service as a pejorative phrase is to demean the most valuable service that medicine has offered the community since one caveman first removed a thorn from another caveman's foot.

THE DIRTIEST GAME IN TOWN

I SWITCHED ON the television set in my hotel room and found Kenneth Clarke, Minister of Health, addressing the 1984 Tory conference. I'd been out of the country for just two weeks and he seemed to have undergone a dramatic conversion.

"Here is an evil which can and must be beaten . . . We will treat the victims, and we will warn the vulnerable, but we must also tackle the evil itself. . . . Dealing in addictive drugs is not a crime of passion or hot blood but a cold-blooded premeditated act by people who know the drugs can kill. . . . Society has to mark its abhorrence of the cold and calculating people who cynically prey on the lives of others for profit."

For one mad moment, I thought he'd decided to act against the cold and calculating people who account for a third of cancer deaths in Britain.

"We cannot have our society, a free and open one, living under the threat of such a dangerous craze."

He was, of course, talking about heroin but every word he used emphasized the hypocrisy that characterizes official attitudes to cigarette smoking. His "evil pushers" do not apparently include those who strive so diligently to addict young people to a drug that will kill one in four of its users before their time. Cigarette salesmen don't like to be reminded that they're "pushers". They prefer their own word-games. They talk of the "controversy" that surrounds their product, suggesting that doubt exists about its lethality (it doesn't), just as they talk of the "argument" about cigarettes which suggests that few experts agree about the value of the evidence. The words crop up so regularly I wonder whether a public relations firm has supplied a glossy directory of "recommended" phrases.

Cigarettes are Britain's most pernicious health hazard, killing some 100,000 Britons every year. Yet every year the fight to eliminate this totally avoidable hazard grows tougher. One reason is a change that has occurred within the tobacco industry. When the lethal effect of cigarettes was first revealed, the captains of the industry were clearly shocked and poured money into research in the hope of finding the cancer-producing ingredient and eliminating it. That hope has since been squashed and the industry is now run by people who have chosen to stay in the business even though they must know, because they are intelligent, that they are peddling a drug that kills. Theirs is the nastiest game you will find in this book. Cigarettes are quite unlike any of the other dangerous products that are sold legally, and with whose vendors the tobacco peddlers like to compare themselves when they lobby for political support.

Alcohol, cars, and motor cycles kill when they are misused. Cigarettes kill when they are used as recommended. There is no safe way to consume them.

One effect of the industry being run by people prepared to accept the lethality of their trade is that the business of dealing with the opposition to cigarettes—and countering the under-funded activities of health educators and individual doctors—has become a sophisticated marketing operation, backed by enormous resources. And, thanks to the money it earns from pushing its drug, the industry wields great political power. It is one of the nastiest scandals of our time that political lobbying and mischief-making are still allowed to protect an industry that peddles an addictive substance even more dangerous than some other "substances" peddled on our streets without benefit of protection from the law.

Since 1984 the BMA has been campaigning vigorously for a ban on all advertising and promotion of cigarettes. One healthy side-effect of such a ban would be to rid us of the official hypocrisy, cant, double dealing, and, let's face it, corruption that we now have to endure. Promoters and televisers of sport, for instance, are made party to cynical and flagrant breaches of the "voluntary agreements" that the tobacco industry has signed to restrict the promotion of cigarettes. The next time you watch televised sport remember that a voluntary agreement bans the display of brand names on participants, officials, or equipment likely to come within range of the cameras. Decent people who administer sport and the arts, or who take part in sport or in sponsored plays and concerts, get entangled in a web of conspiracy that also enmeshes the BBC and ITA. And all to help addict people to a drug that kills.

Peddling cigarettes is the dirtiest game in town. Doctors get involved only because they want to clean it up. Yet, whenever they try, politicians, who know what's best for the rest of us, tell them to resume their seats in the spectators' stand.

Peter Taylor, a BBC *Panorama* reporter, has supplied, in his book *Smoke Ring: The Politics of Tobacco*, a detailed account of the political chicanery stimulated by the cigarette business. He describes, for instance, how Sir George Young, once Mrs Thatcher's health minister, lost the job when he wanted to ban cigarette advertising and promotion. Sir Anthony Kershaw,

British American Tobacco's paid parliamentary consultant told Taylor: "He was moved ... There would have been a major political row about a peripheral political matter at a time when the government was deeply unpopular and the recession was very bad. This is the political reality." Sir George Young was replaced by Kenneth Clarke whose constituency is in Nottingham, home of John Player, and who had already declared himself a supporter of tobacco-sponsorship of sport. Small wonder that some of us suffered a twinge of nausea when he won cheers from the faithful at his party conference with his selective condemnation of those who try to addict young people to a drug that can kill.

Like all profitable drug rackets, the peddling of cigarettes generates corruption around it.

Corruption isn't too extravagant a word to describe the way, for instance, so many people connive at the cynical breaching of agreements made to save lives. Or the way MPs use phrases like "political reality" to justify the killing of people to protect the income of the Exchequer or the profits of their friends. Or the way newspapers treat the tobacco industry more favourably than they do industries with lower advertising budgets. Or the way a Department of "Health" fails to take the most effective single step available to it to prevent disease.

Banning the promotion of cigarettes would purify the air in ways other than the literal.

A NEW IMPROVED KILLING GAME

In 1983, I emerged from a few weeks of scribbling in my garret, to discover that political conversation had switched from electioneering to the more wholesome topic of hanging—of the by-the-neck-until-dead variety. Indeed, Mr Harry Allen, Britain's official hangman, had announced, not without a hint of enthusiasm, that he was "still available".

I learned this one morning when researchers from two different television companies solicited my views on how modern medical techniques could improve judicial killing, not to make it any less effective—no one wants half dead criminals clutter-

ing up our jails—but, as one of them said on the phone "to
make it less, how can I put it, doctor, messy." I explained that
most doctors I knew were too busy trying to keep people alive
to have time for a little official killing on the side, and suggested
that a more appropriate despatcher might be one of those
bishops who had declared themselves in favour of the rope.
After all, why stop at preparing a poor sinner to meet his Maker
when you have the opportunity actually to speed him on his
way?

Soon after those phone calls, the House of Commons voted
against the restoration of hanging, but opinion polls suggest
that most Britons would still like to bring it back so maybe we
doctors should apply our minds to the matter, after all. One
thing is clear. If hanging is restored it will not be to wreak
vengeance, to appease the Gods, to banish heresy, or for any
other traditional reason. It will be restored because people
believe it is a deterrent. That being so, I suggest we apply
our imaginations to devising ways of enhancing its deterrent
quality. Clearly we will never realize its full potential if we
continue to hang people surreptitiously in the privacy of our
own prisons. If execution is to deter, it must once again become
a public spectacle. I acknowledge that this poses some logistical
problems. In London, for instance, it could prove difficult to
provide adequate parking facilities around Tyburn without
curtailing the amenities of a Royal Park. And while Manchester
has an ideal site, Old Trafford would be available only when
United were playing away and they would likely take most of
the potential audience with them. Still these are only details
and because a resolute nation will not let them stand in its
way, I feel encouraged to put forward a modest proposal.

These days "privatization", though an ugly word, is an
eagerly embraced political idea. So why don't we sell off exclusive promotional rights in our public executions to some
entrepreneurial organization that could make them not only
an effective deterrent but could, in the jargon of their trade,
"realize their full profit potential". I have no particular organization in mind. I don't think it matters what it is as long as it
has a good track record: maybe one of those agencies that
represents "sporting personalities" and television presenters,
or the organizers of *Miss World*.

The key to deterrence—and profitability—will lie in the sale of exclusive television coverage. Not only will this make it a truly public event but a global hook-up will enable us to pass on the deterrent benefit to societies less advanced than our own —to those earnest Scandinavian countries, for instance, where they all seem to take life so seriously.

Sponsorship should prove no problem. I'm sure a tobacco company would snap up the opportunity and its flags and hoardings would create a wholly appropriate ambience. Perhaps the hapless felon—who would need to be renamed "executee"—could be persuaded to wear a costume echoing the designs of a cigarette advertisement, just like other participants in televised sports.

The more I think about it, the more I see one of Britain's Traditional Occasions: the traditional marching display by the massed bands of something or other, the traditional baritone of yesteryear leading the bare-headed crowd in the traditional "Abide with me" as the executee is guided to the gallows by the traditional topless Page Three Girl. Back in the studio, the traditional panel of experts: A Bishop, A Doctor, A Woman, and the chairman of the British Ropemakers' Federation, would offer pre- and post-mortem comments. And, of course, later in the evening we could see edited highlights on "Drop of the Day". Properly handled, the affair could have all the colourful appeal of It's a Knockout without the underlying streak of violence.

Which brings us back to the problem that the television researchers raised with me. In televisual terms, hanging is a bit messy and I'm sure it won't be easy to see exactly what's going on, even with the aid of action replays. So how could we doctors "improve" on it?

After a deal of thought I've decided the neatest solution would be beheading: swift, surgical, effective, and traditional. Come to think of it, Bring Back the Axe would make a handy slogan for political campaigners.

Anyone know the telephone number of Saatchi and Saatchi?

Dressing up games

OPERATIC DOCTORS

WHAT MAKES A doctor? Most actors settle for a pin-striped suit and a hint of greying over the temporoparietal muscles. They end up looking like aging repertory playboys. Which indeed many of them are. Margaret Stacey, a professor of sociology, has suggested that the pathognomonic characteristic of a doctor is clean finger nails but I suspect we reveal our identity less in our appearance than in our behaviour.

One of the most convincing portrayals of a doctor I've seen on the stage was in, of all things, an opera . . . possibly because the director was a proper off-stage doctor. The occasion was the Kent Opera production of *La Traviata* and the director was Jonathan Miller. The on-stage doctor, who appears in the last act to serve the traditional operatic purpose of prognosing the imminent triumph of tubercle, looked like a doctor because of one simple piece of production. He didn't, as the character often does, stand beside Violetta's bed and gaze down on her while he chanted a few unconvincing lies

Then we must take heart . . .
Convalescence is not far away . . .

In the Jonathan Miller production he sat on the side of her bed and put his hand on her wrist not just to take her pulse but to establish human contact while he offered words that he and Violetta knew were only words. Her acknowledgement of their real meaning—"Doctors are allowed a pious fib"—was a painfully accurate echo of a moment familiar to clinicians.

That actor's doctor-like qualities were so convincing that a scene that is usually played as a time filler while the audience —and Violetta—draw breath and prepare themselves for a melodic shuffling off of the coils, became one of the most poignant moments of the evening.

Doctors in opera don't often get a chance like that to steal a scene. But then they're an odd lot. I'm never happy, for instance, about the ethical behaviour of the doctor in the last act of *La Bohème* who accepts Musetta's earrings as pre-payment for a visit. I don't condemn him for not making it to the garret before the final curtain—that could happen to any busy GP—but I don't think he should send "a cordial" on ahead of him. It smacks too much of prescribing for a patient he hasn't seen. Maybe he guesses that because she's an opera singer—he may even have heard her belting out her reprise of "Che gelida manina" across the rooftops of Paris—it's just another routine case of terminal pthisis.

The most irritating of operatic doctors is surely the one in Verdi's *Macbeth* who is addicted to the question mark. Once his scene gets under way, his lines, apart from four "Oh, horror!"s, are all questions to the maid: "What did she speak of in her sleep?", "She carries a light in her hands?", "How wide open are her eyes?", "Why does she rub her hands?", "What did she say?", "She sighs?", and "This too?". And all but the first of these are asked while the lady in question is singing none too quietly just a couple of yards away from him. Most of his patients must have expired while he was still interrogating the servants.

His on-stage behaviour loses credibility when contrasted with the off-stage behaviour of a real doctor during a performance of the same opera at Glyndebourne. The doctor was there because the singer playing Banquo, the late David Franklin, was suffering from renal colic. In the story, as David used to tell it, the treatment that sustained him was morphine to dull the pain, benzedrine to counter the depressive effect of the morphine, and champagne because John Christie thought it was good for everything. David managed to keep going till the first interval but had to be carried to his dressing room where the doctor examined him with some concern. Mrs Franklin, watching anxiously, was worried by the doctor's demeanour.

"Should he really go back on?" she asked.

"What's he got to do in this next Act?" asked the doctor.

"A death scene."

"He'll do that all right," said the doctor.

Modern medicine's most dramatic contribution to opera was surely that made in 1961 by a party of local medical students recruited to play the walk-on firing squad in the last act of *Tosca* at the San Francisco opera house. The students, chosen for height rather than stage experience, knew nothing of the opera or its plot, and the producer, who was having problems with one of the principals, had little time to brief them. He wasn't worried because they didn't have to sing. Five minutes before the start of the dress rehearsal, he told them: "You're a firing squad. Just follow the officer. Slow march on in time to the music, line up and, when the officer lowers his sword, shoot."

"And how do we get off?"

"Just wait on stage and, at the end, exit with the principals."

The dress rehearsal ran out of time and never reached the final scene so, on the first night, the San Francisco audience saw *Tosca* end in an unusual way.

When, at the tragic denouement, the firing squad marched slowly on, its members were momentarily confused by the fact that there were both a man and a woman on stage. However when Cavaradossi stepped bravely in front of them they decided he was the one they had to shoot. Yet as they lined up their sights they noticed he kept nodding in a conspiratorial way towards the woman. So, as the officer dropped his sword, they swung their rifles through 180 degrees and shot Tosca.

They were clearly discomfited when she remained standing and they heard Cavaradossi, now directly behind them, hit the stage as he dropped. They gawped nervously as Tosca rushed to him, spoke to him as if he were still alive, and then screamed. And they began to grow panicky when they heard the shouts off-stage and saw Tosca mount the battlements. Then, as she flung herself off, they remembered their final instruction. As the curtain slowly descended, they rushed upstage and threw themselves after her.

I sometimes wonder how they made out as doctors.

TOY SOLDIERS

WHEN I JOINED our citizen army as a national service doctor in 1954, I detected an incompatibility between the army and medicine. Soon after my call-up I found myself in the midst of a vast parade on St Martin's Plain just outside Folkestone. From where I stood, safely anonymous in the middle ranks, it was an impressive sight: serried ranks, bayonets fixed, flags flying, bands playing, and lots of people stamping their feet and shouting.

Thanks to some strange quirk of military protocol, one of the four officers standing out in front of the parade was a national service doctor from the local military hospital. The three proper officers had crisply pressed uniforms and a shine on their shoes that seemed as unnatural as the way the peaks of their caps were rammed on to the bridges of their noses. The doctor wore a rumpled battledress and suede shoes and his RAMC cap was perched uneasily on a mound of frizzy hair.

Then, as the general who had come to inspect us ascended his podium and the RSM bellowed a loud incoherent command at us all, the doctor looked impatiently at his watch and strolled casually off the parade.

Next morning when wheeled in front of an apopleptic brigadier, he explained he was already seven minutes late for his clinic and didn't want to keep his patients waiting.

He wasn't playing a game. You could tell the conscript doctors from the regulars by their attitude to medicine. Most conscripts had been drafted soon after qualifying and were keen as mustard on their new craft. The "regular" doctors who'd spent most of their professional lives looking after healthy young men were more *dégagé*. The best of the regulars were honest about their clinical limitations and admitted they had joined the RAMC to get away from the drudgery of clinical practice. The CO of one hospital—a kindly, soft-voiced Dubliner—once told me: "I expect my junior officers to get on with the medicine. I specialize in Good Living." He'd joined the Indian Army medical service in the nineteen-thirties and, when he went aboard his troopship at Southampton, his only baggage was two polo saddles. He was a useful antidote to the earnestness of conscripts whom medical schools had so recently taught to know everything.

Some of his regular colleagues had more dangerous pretensions. A national service friend of mine, hidden behind screens while examining a patient, overheard what he defined as the "regular's indication for surgery". A passing regular said to a colleague: "I hope they call me in on that case. I haven't been inside a chest for years."

Once I'd accepted that the RAMC was a two-year break from proper medicine, the incongruities grew entertaining. After a year in Folkestone, I was given yellow-fever injections, issued with tropical kit, and posted to East Grinstead where my new CO promoted me to Major on the charitable grounds that he had to have one and I was the person most in need of the extra pay.

In the summer of 1955 the IRA raided the REME armoury at Arborfield and made off with guns and ammunition. At the time I was billeted with an RASC unit and, the day after the Arborfield raid, my hosts left camp to do their summer weekend job of bungling up the roads between London and the south coast with convoys of inexperienced drivers. My CO was on leave and when a despatch rider arrived at the barracks demanding to see the senior officer present, guess who that was? He handed me a message, too hot to be sent by telephone, ordering the recipient to collect top-secret instructions on how to secure our armoury against IRA attacks. I had to collect the instructions personally from the Home Counties District signals office in Folkestone.

That posed a problem. The evening before, deciding that the Russians were unlikely to invade over the weekend, I'd sent my only uniform to the cleaners. But the despatch rider was waiting for a reply and I had to compose one that sounded neither suspicious nor facetious. How would you explain that the only man available to collect an anti-IRA plan was a doctor who had no right to be a Major, whose name was O'Donnell, and who was turning up in mufti because he'd mislaid his uniform?

In the end, I settled for a simple scrawled note saying I'd drop in after dinner, round about half-past nine. Only after my message—I beg its pardon, signal—was on its way did I think it might have read better if I'd written 2130. As it happened, I was a bit late because I stopped off to see my parents-in-law midway between East Grinstead and Folkestone. We had a splendid dinner. My mother-in-law was quietly proud of the crowns that would have been on my shoulders if they hadn't been at the cleaners and my father-in-law rustled up some decent claret. By the time I reached Folkestone, I was comfortably aglow. I took a short cut across the camp where I'd lived for a year, parked outside the signals office, and went in. I found a large room crammed with radios, field telephones and teleprinters, amid which wandered a bespectacled lance-corporal with a pencil behind his ear.

"I'm Dr O'Donnell," I said. "I've come for the signal for Hobbs Barracks."

He was clearly a fellow national serviceman because he slipped straight into the conversational mode I'd used.

"Can't give it to you, I'm afraid. Sergeant has to hand it over and he nipped out five minutes back. I don't reckon he'll be long."

"Not to worry," I said, and then jumped as two telex machines behind me chattered into life.

"Gone bloody mad tonight," said my friend.

While we waited for the sergeant, he showed me round, explaining how the decoders and the scramblers worked, and digging among the top-secret files for examples of the prep-school humour with which the Intelligence chaps at Maresfield laced their reports on putative "subversives".

The door burst open and in marched the sergeant, stamping his highly polished boots across the lino. Suddenly I was gazing in terror down the barrel of a revolver.

"Identification?" barked the sergeant.

I fished my identity card from my pocket with trembling hand. He examined it carefully, then lowered his gun. .

"Major O'Donnell. Hobbs Barracks. We wondered what happened to you, sir. Do you mind telling me how you got through our security cordon?"

"I drove up Horn Street and came in the back way."

"That explains it." He looked relieved. "If you'd tried to come through the main entrance, we'd have got you."

Scientific games

THE FLEXIBLE DOGMA GAME

ARTICLES OF FAITH seem to be making a come-back, if not in church at least on breakfast television. When the BBC started its morning service, we could, if we got up early enough on a Thursday morning, get a word of advice from a doctor. We had less difficulty catching the resident astrologer who appeared every day predicting the future with a dogmatic certainty that the poor quack, tethered by reason, could never hope to match. Commenting on the phenomenon in *The List-ener*, Karl Sabbagh wondered what our reaction would be if the BBC forecasted the weather by examining lumps of seaweed.

More recently Dr Shawn Carlson of the University of California has concluded two exhaustive investigations of astrological interpretations that he set up with the co-operation of astrologers highly regarded within their trade. He employed the "double blind" techniques that are used to measure the effectiveness of new drugs and, after three years' investigation, concluded: "Despite the fact that we worked with some of the best astrologers . . . despite the fact they approved of the design of the experiment and predicted 50 per cent as the minimum effect they would expect to see, astrology failed to perform at a level better than chance. Tested, using double-blind methods, the astrologers' predictions proved to be wrong."

That, of course, is the sort of boring conclusion you're likely to get from doctors and could be the reason why the BBC decided that what people want with their cornflakes is not fact but faith.

I have a suspicion that the BBC is right. Over the past month,

for instance, I've been asked did I believe—not had I examined
the evidence but did I believe—not just in astrology but in
copper bracelets for rheumatism, natural childbirth, coronary
by-pass surgery, and a First Division future for Manchester
City. (Why I wonder do people never question my faith in less
substantial propositions like the existence of Brian Inglis or of
trains on the Bakerloo Line during the rush hour?)

Only the question about Manchester City was acceptable.
Football long ago ceased to be a game and became the centre
of doctrinal disputation, largely because the participants share
an unquestioning belief in the power of good and evil. When
the lads do well, it is because they believe in themselves. When
they do badly, it is the work of the devil. In the words of the
liturgy, the score, the referee's decision, or the referee himself
was diabolical.

In this age of irrational faith, a wise man keeps an eye on
his beliefs. Many of life's comforts, like membership of the right
clubs or access to patronage, depend on a chap carrying, or
appearing to carry, the right beliefs in his knapsack. If you
want to get on in medicine, for instance, it's safer to be considered "sound" rather than clever. And the best way to build a
reputation for soundness is to cultivate the air of a man who holds
all the right beliefs but is modestly reluctant to express them.

The principle stays true if you want to make your name as
a rebel save that you must change your knapsack more often
and show off its contents whenever you can. Doctors who want
to be known as outsiders or as "a bit of an original thinker"
soon learn that flexibility is as important as publicity.
They must never let themselves be hobbled to yesterday's
dogma. Whatever happened to Ivan Illich or, for that matter,
Sir Alf Ramsey?

Yesterday's dogma is particularly dangerous in medicine.
These days, for instance, to gain acceptance as a progressive
obstetrician you need to campaign for more home confinements,
to disparage epidural anaesthesia as a grossly overused inter-
ference with a natural process, and condemn bottle feeding as
a monstrosity almost as grave as infanticide. Yet just over
twenty years ago a progressive obstetrician was expected to
abuse reactionaries who criticized plans to have all women
delivered in "safer" hospital beds, and had to champion every

woman's right to painless childbirth and to free herself from the tyranny of breast feeding. In those days, of course, few of us would have admitted that we made such things as acts of faith. Our quirks were not a matter of belief but of rational deduction made only after "objective" scientific observation.

The mission of post-war progressives was to sweep anecdotal mumblings from medical journals and replace them with dispassionate "facts". Ours was not an age for seers and witch doctors. They had had a good run in the twenties and thirties, the years of the "toxic focus", childhood "acidosis" and high colonic lavage. The Uri Gellers of our day—a thought-reading act called the Piddingtons—didn't dare claim they possessed mysterious paranormal powers. They won our attention by telling us they were tricksters and challenging us to guess how they worked their illusions.

I suspect it was our earnestness that caused the pendulum to swing. Certainly we strangled the journals as researcher after tedious researcher explained in attenuated detail how he or she had proved that black was black and that white was white. Small wonder people switched to the soft option of simple faith.

A few years ago, Jon Tinker, discussing in the *New Scientist* whether or not we should "believe" in the Loch Ness monster, described why there was little hope of détente between believers and infidels. "If the Nessie debunkers will never be satisfied with anything less than a corpse, the pro-monster faction is unlikely to be defeated on theoretical grounds. Rather like the existence of God." I fear he's right but find it sad that he leaves no room for agnosticism. This is no age for those of us for whom the only certainty is doubt. We run the danger of being trampled into the mud as all around us leap to their feet "to be counted". Faiths don't allow for proportional representation. No longer can we say, with the Irish philosopher: "We are all atheists now, thank God."

THE AUTHORITARIAN GAME

IN THE LAND of Academe, science has built its own cathedrals. Indeed, so many impressive, even stately, institutions now exist to shelter the faithful that it's easy to forget that science is essentially a subversive trade.

The majesty of many scientific institutions, and their power, have helped create a paradox. Although scientific inquiry is by nature an anti-authoritarian game, many people now see scientists as protectors of orthodoxy—as persons whose eyes are closed to "the needs of the people", whose ears are deaf to the seductive pleas of alternative views.

One effect this paradox can have on medicine is illustrated in an incident recorded by Iain Chalmers, director of the National Perinatal Epidemiology Unit in Oxford. He had been impressed by Michel Odent's suggestion that some elements of the formal preparation for childbirth might jeopardize a woman's ability to discover for herself how best to cope during labour. So, during a meeting on pregnancy and childbirth, he asked one of the speakers, a childbirth educator, what scientific evidence she could provide to reassure him that the sort of antenatal education she advocated did not make women's labours more difficult.

He wasn't denying that antenatal education was helpful but, like any good scientist, was testing the credentials of a received truth. The woman reacted in the traditional style of authority when challenged. She said she had a profound distrust of scientific research and epitomized her view of it with a description of baby monkeys being tortured while their mothers went berserk on the other side of a glass screen.

Chalmers concedes that the "Auschwitz" view of scientific inquiry has been fostered by some of the appalling things done to animals—and humans—in the name of research. Yet that view of science so dominates public thinking that people have forgotten that the purpose of science is to question authority and actively to foster uncertainty. We expand our knowledge by questioning present "certainties" but Chalmers has described* how, in his own area of medicine, the authoritarian game played by both "mainstream" and "alternative" enthusiasts obstructs the full exploitation of the scientific method in the interests of women and children.

"The problem is not that those engaged in public debate about care during pregnancy and childbirth always ignore

* Chalmers I. "Scientific Inquiry and Authoritarianism in Perinatal Care and Education". *Birth* 1983; 10:151–164

scientific evidence. It is that they tend to allude to it when it suits them to do so. They frequently use the debating tactic of pointing out that the views of their opponents are unsupported by scientific evidence." Yet, says, Chalmers, they too often operate a double standard over the quality of evidence they require of those with whom they disagree and the evidence they use themselves to substantiate their claims. He provides a list of the defensive strategies that authoritarian game players use when faced by impudent challenge. They include:

It is unethical to withhold (or use) the intervention.

The results of the research are uninteresting or irrelevant.

If the results are not to our liking, then the sample was too small or the bathwater was at the wrong temperature.

If we like the results, never mind the sample size. "We told you so."

If we don't like the results, the investigators are incompetent, dishonest, or fascist.

In Britain the last of those strategies can be implemented with a special vocabulary. Thanks to our caste system, players have a rich fund of words they can use to label opponents and so write off their views. They can be labelled as "unsound", "a bit of a show-off", "too big for their boots" (most often used by persons who are too small for theirs), "too clever by half" . . . and so on. Such phrases are most effective when used at a dinner table or other social gathering where they can be lobbed, in a half-whisper, from a corner of the mouth into a receptive ear.

Doctors face a particular dilemma over their use of the scientific method. They need to employ it to protect their patients by challenging authoritarian certainties that are promulgated about their care. Yet, as Chalmers points out, the active promotion of uncertainty which science demands, can seriously disable those who are expected to speak and act with confidence.

Richard Asher[†] described the clinician's dilemma:

If you can believe fervently in your treatment, even though controlled tests show that it is quite useless, then your results are much better, your patients are much better, and your

[†] Asher R. *Richard Asher Talking-sense.* Avery Jones F, ed. London: Pitman Medical, 1972:48

income is much better too. I believe this accounts for the remarkable success of some of the less gifted but more credulous members of our profession, and also for the violent dislike of statistics and controlled tests which fashionable and successful doctors are accustomed to display. It is an almost insoluble problem and the majority of worthwhile doctors are driven to a compromise in which they muster enough genuine belief in their treatment to keep their patients happy and maintain their own self-respect, while preserving enough doubt to admit their inadequacy during transient bouts of uncomfortable honesty.

The dilemma certainly exists and doctors who play the authoritarian game need to retain insight into what they are doing. Some of them don't and Chalmers quotes work that suggests that medical students' ability to assess the quality of evidence used to support authoritarian claims actually deteriorates as they come into increasing contact with clinical teachers.

Clearly, we need to find some way of sneaking more subversive thinkers into our medical schools.

EDITH AND THE APOCALYPTICS

I WRITE THIS in a small room in a small town that lies near the Western border of New York State. Round the corner from where I sit is Main Street and, when I strolled along it half an hour ago, its most memorable feature was a white-painted shop with a name-board that read: "Grindle's. Computer outlet and nose clippers". I am, you will gather, firmly ensconced in Middle America.

It's a good place to reflect on a lecture I attended yesterday in a city some 400 miles to the West, and try to decide whether I saw the beginnings of what they call in these parts a "backlash" or merely the hype of a new book. If it is a backlash, many doctors will welcome it because it is against a form of unreason with which science, technology, and indeed industry, have had to contend for the past 25 years.

The creator of yesterday's stir was Edith Efron, a journalist who is now a research associate at the University of Rochester School of Management. Her book, published in the USA, is called *The Apocalyptics: Cancer and the Big Lie* and she describes its theme thus:

> For several decades—since the publication of *Silent Spring* by Rachel Carson—our nation's efforts to combat cancer have been dominated by a religious-political view of man, nature, and society.
>
> I call the environmental scientists and government regulators who adhere to this ideology "The Apocalyptics", in that with little or no data, they have ceaselessly projected the catastrophic destruction of life on earth by industrial civilization. Where apocalyptics are concerned, cancer is fundamentally a modern moral and political disease caused by the human evils of intellectual arrogance and greed.
>
> Ninety per cent of it, they have said, comes from "the Faustian sin"; from man's arrogant conquest of nature; from post-World War Two science, technology, economic growth, and affluence; from the primary values of the industrial revolution and Western civilization and, not infrequently, from capitalism, the market, and profits.

She canonizes Rachel Carson as patron saint of the Apocalyptics and lists among her disciples Barry Commoner, Paul Ehrlich, René Dubois, Samuel Epstein, and Ralph Nader. But what she really indicts is a mood, a way of thinking—maybe even a religion—that I suspect took a tighter grip on the imagination of Middle America than on that of Middle Britain.

Miss Efron claims she read some 15,000 scientific papers and 500 books in the course of her research and has little difficulty finding scientific fact to shoot down the fancies of American environmentalists who, during the 1970s, issued repeated alarms of impending disaster. Yesterday I enjoyed occasional glows of chauvinistic pride when she referred to the work of the Oxford Richards—Sir Richard Doll and Richard Peto—each time she wanted to show what science had actually established.

I can but hint at the weight of evidence she adduces in her book. At one point, for instance, she documents the way that those who've played the apocalyptic game have focussed attention on industrial chemicals and food additives and have insidiously suggested that few carcinogens came from the Garden of Eden. She then prints a 40-page list of naturally occurring carcinogens. (It reminded me of Sir Richard Doll's remark: "So many things can cause cancer, it's a lucky person who gets out of this world alive.")

She also supplies a string of documented case histories that show how official bodies have been swept into the apocalyptic game. Typical of these is her description of how, in 1980, the FDA denied a petition from Abbott Laboratories to have cyclamates reapproved. Abbott submitted data showing that only one bladder tumour occurred among 520 heavily dosed rats—the known spontaneous incidence of that type of tumour in that type of rat. Any rational scientist, she suggests, would accept that data as impressive evidence of safety but the FDA claimed it was evidence of a weak carcinogenic effect and told Abbot that, to show that cyclamates were safe "with reasonable certainty", they would need to test another 100,000 animals. That would have cost another 100 million dollars so Americans were denied a product used widely—and apparently safely— in Europe.

Miss Efron assembles formidable evidence to support her case. Why then do I have reservations about the performance she put on yesterday for an audience of international science writers and research scientists? The reason, I fear, was her style, which too often verged on the—dare I say it?—apocalyptic. Time and again, for instance, she suggested that for twenty years American scientists and American journalists had conspired to keep the truth from the American people. And time and again she distracted the attention of her audience from the strength of her case by blaming manifestations of public ignorance or of official incompetence on that conspiracy.

I just cannot believe that in the USA, of all places, such a gigantic confidence trick could have been played. I doubt that even the Russians could pull it off on their home ground. I find it easier to believe that the apocalyptic game grew out of a prevailing fashion of thought rather than a political conspiracy.

It will be a pity if Miss Efron's style deafens her audience to what she is actually saying. The arguments she uses need to be heard—and I believe people are now prepared to listen to them, particularly in the USA. Americans seem to find it easier than Britons to admit they have made a mistake. They just say "We goofed", change their attitude, and continue cheerfully on their way without having to indulge in that tortuous self-justification which we Britons deem essential before changing our minds.

Middle America seems a sensible, if naive, community ... though I confess to unease at the thought of those nose clippers.

INVESTIGATING MAGIC

MY THOUGHTS THESE days are often with those BMA persons who've been chosen to investigate the claims of Alternative Medicine; almost as often as they are with the persons whose alternative practices are being examined.

What happens if these practices win the BMA seal of approval? With the loss of their claim to be Alternative, they could lose one of their strongest selling points. They would certainly lose their attraction for iconoclastic devotees who find truth only in unorthodoxy.

I also wonder whether the BMA, while it's in the mood, will examine some of the practices still indulged in the name of orthodox medicine. It's not only Alternative Medicine that attracts venal practitioners prepared to exploit our natural gullibility to make themselves rich. I suppose it's too late for the BMA to duck out and pass these questions to the new professor of parapsychology in Edinburgh. But it might not be too late to ensure the investigative team includes not just scientists but professional magicians.

The history of the last hundred years suggests that professional magicians and "conjurers" (a useful word that seems to have slipped from fashion) are more effective detectors of fraud than professional scientists. Gullible scientists told us that Uri Geller had strange psychokinetic powers that could change the physical properties of metal (powers which he turned to such socially useful purposes as bending teaspoons); less gullible magicians revealed him as one of their own. Anyone who, as a child, possessed a "Junior Conjurer's Set"

Will have learned two simple lessons about magic. Audiences long to be deceived and are invariably disappointed when they are told how the trick is done.

The Magic Circle adjures its members not to reveal their secrets not just because there is a limited number of "magical" devices (most "tricks" are variations on about half a dozen) but because, when the secret of a trick is revealed, it nearly always disappoints. The secret is usually simple, barefaced, and banal and contrasts uneasily with the wonder generated by a well-performed illusion. The great magicians are those who, using this mundane trickery beneath a camouflage of showmanship and misdirection, can convince an audience it has witnessed something that defies rational understanding.

It's not by chance that conjurer's instruction leaflets start by describing The Effect which is what the audience thinks it sees happening. Only a couple of paragraphs later, under The Method, do we read what actually does happen—a bit of barefaced deception from which the audience's attention is diverted, often by exploitation of its longing to be deceived. (Magicians learned to use the placebo effect long before doctors recognized that it existed.)

When scientists examine phenomena that are beyond our comprehension they tend to concentrate on The Effect, analysing it, dissecting it, hypothesizing about it. A professional magician, out of habit, goes straight for possible Methods and is unimpressed by anecdotal evidence of the Effect the audience thought it saw. Magicians are also better than scientists at persuading audiences that deception has taken place. They can reproduce the same Effects as the fraudulent operators by using the simple devices of their trade and announce not how the trick was done—which would merely disappoint—but that it was no more magical than the illusions in their stage acts. Audiences find these demonstrations more convincing than intellectual arguments. Harry Houdini used them to expose fraudulent "mediums" in days when seances were more fashionable than they are now. The Amazing Randi still uses them to challenge tricksters more likely to be found these days on television chat shows than in back rooms in Brooklyn.

A few years ago I learned just how effective the magician's method of exposure can be. In the days when "psychokinetic metal bending" colonized much time on television and much space in scientific journals, I persuaded one of Britain's best science writers, a highly intelligent and talented fellow with a doctorate in one of the "harder" sciences, to re-examine his new-found belief in this form of "psychokinesis". And I persuaded him not by intellectual argument but by performing a mundane card trick that I learned when I was a member of the Magic Circle. The trick had nothing to do with metal bending or psychokinesis and he still doesn't know how I did it, but the fact that such "magic" could be performed by an ignorant oaf like me re-established the sense of scepticism he had temporarily mislaid.

Scepticism is essential when evaluating treatment. Most people who seek cures are not interested in arguments about schools of thought and logic. They are interested in results. And the most impressive way to present results is in the form of testimonials from satisfied customers. Yet anyone who's done any sort of service job knows just how easy it is to acquire

flattering testimonials. When I was a GP, I had drawerfuls of grateful letters from patients who had survived my ministrations thanks more to their luck than to my judgement. Anyone who treats patients can earn similar tributes thanks to the body's vigorous powers of self-healing.

In conjurer's terms testimonials relate only to The Effect. Scientific investigation concerns itself with The Method.

In 1983, in the *New England Journal of Medicine*, a Californian physician, Faith Fitzgerald, recorded her experience of a series of television and radio appearances in which she had had to confront some of the progenitors of "nontraditional" medicine and their disciples. She describes three sorts of person with whom doctors, educated to assume that "reason, logic, and common sense interpretation of the obvious are the prevalent modes of human thought," find it difficult to communicate, and whom they are therefore unlikely to persuade. The first is the True Believer whose adherence to a particular therapy has become a religious faith and thus unamenable to scientific reason. The second is The Mercantalist, the con artist, whose main motivation is greed. Says Dr Fitzgerald: "The only argument one can mobilize against these frauds is loss of profits or fear of punishment. To dispute the scientific merit of what they're peddling makes no impression, so long as it sells." Her third class of person forms The Audience whose allegiance, she found, was not to logic but to efficacy. "Magic was as acceptable as reason, so long as it accomplished what was promised."

When the BMA produces its report, the public which will examine its findings is the audience which Dr Fitzgerald describes, I believe accurately, as "basically pragmatic, with less loyalty to logic or to schools of thought than to results." And that is why I suggest that if the BMA enquiry wishes to differentiate between honest and less honest practices conducted under the banner of "Alternative Medicine", it should consider co-opting a professional magician. His, or her, presence could liven discussion and guide the doctors' doctors through the game they need to play.

For, when the report is published, the audience may well find a magical performance more persuasive than intellectual argument from learned doctors.